GENETICS & EVOLUTION

David Barrett
B.Sc., C.Biol., M.I. Biol., P.G.C.E.
Housemaster, Clifton College Bristol;
Chief Examiner and Examiner of
A-Level projects in Biology
&
Paul Spencer
B.Sc. Head of Science, Thorpe
St Andrews School, Norwich

Nelson Blackie

Thomas Nelson and Sons Ltd
Nelson House Mayfield Road
Walton-on-Thames Surrey
KT12 5PL

51 York Place
Edinburgh
EH1 3JD

Nelson Blackie
Westercleddens Road
Bishopbriggs
Glasgow
G64 2NZ

Thomas Nelson (Hong Kong) Ltd
Toppan Building 10/F
22A Westlands Road
Quarry Bay Hong Kong

Thomas Nelson Australia
102 Dodds Street
South Melbourne
Victoria 3205 Australia

Nelson Canada
1120 Birchmount Road
Scarborough Ontario
M1K 5G4 Canada

ISBN 0-17-448197-7
NPN 9 8 7 6 5 4 3 2

ACKNOWLEDGEMENTS

Photographic material

Hulton Picture Company 1, 48; Kings College London Archives 2; Science Photo Library 2, 10, 81 (top), 89, 91; Alan Cadogan 31 (top), 37 (left and right); Frank Lane Picture Agency 31 (bottom), 90, 93, 94; Cystic Fibrosis Research Trust 34; Agricultural and Food Research Council 65; Cellmark Diagnostics 81 (bottom), 86, 87 (left and right).

The authors would also like to acknowledge the help and advice of the following: Mrs Prue Willday, Dr. Linda Tyfield, geneticist at Southmead Hospital, Bristol.

Cover photo courtesy of Science Photo Library (*Gel electrophoresis viewed under UV light showing bands of DNA*)

Printed in Great Britain by Bell and Bain Ltd., Glasgow

CONTENTS

GENERAL EDITOR'S INTRODUCTION TO THE SERIES (IV)

AUTHORS' INTRODUCTION TO GENETICS (IV)

1 DNA - THE LADDER OF LIFE 1

2 TWO TYPES OF CELL DIVISION 21

3 MEIOSIS AND INHERITANCE 31

4 MENDEL'S EXPERIMENTS 37

5 MENDEL'S CONTRIBUTION TO HUMAN GENETICS 44

6 MORE OF MENDEL AND MATHEMATICS! 59

7 RATIOS, χ^2 AND HARDY-WEINBERG 74

8 DNA ANALYSIS: GENETIC FINGERPRINTING AND GENE TRACKING 81

9 EVOLUTION 88

ANSWERS 98

INDEX 107

General Editor's Introduction to the Series

Biology - Advanced Studies is a series of modular textbooks which are intended for students following advanced courses in biological subjects. The series offers the flexibility essential for working on modern syllabuses which often have core material and option topics. In particular, the books should be very useful for the new modular science courses which are emerging at A-Level.

In most of the titles in the series, one of the authors is a very experienced teacher (often also an examiner) and is sympathetic to the problems of learning at this level. The second author usually has research experience and is familiar with the subject at a higher level. In addition, several members of the writing team have been closely involved in the development of the latest syllabuses.

As with all text books, the reader may expect not to read from cover to cover but to study one topic at a time, or dip-in for information as needed. The index can be used like a science dictionary because where a page number is shown in bold print an explanation or definition will be found in the text. Where questions are asked, an attempt should be made at an answer because this type of *active reading* is the best way to develop an understanding of what is read.

We have referred throughout to *Biological nomenclature - Recommendations on terms, units and symbols*, Institute of Biology, London, 1989. We are delighted to be able to thank the many friends and colleagues who have helped with original ideas, the reading of drafts and the supply of illustrations.

Alan Cadogan
General Editor

Authors' Introduction to Genetics

This book offers a different approach to genetics. The main emphasis is on DNA, with particular reference to how this molecule is involved in producing proteins, whether enzymic or structural. It is these proteins that are fundamental in creating the characteristics that organisms inherit.

Mitosis is merely a way of duplicating DNA, and meiosis is a way of passing on DNA to offspring while, at the same time, creating new combinations of the DNA molecule. Understand how DNA works; how DNA is duplicated and passed on to offspring, and you will then understand how the characteristics determined by DNA are inherited, i.e. you will understand genetics.

Many examples of inherited characteristics have been included in the book and human examples have been given wherever possible. A number of 'in-text' questions are present in this book. These questions should be attempted as you read. You will find answers to some but not all of these questions in the back of the book.

David Barrett and Paul Spencer

CHAPTER 1

DNA - THE LADDER OF LIFE

Watson and Crick with their DNA model

No.4356 April 25 1953 NATURE 737

MOLECULAR STRUCTURE OF NUCLEIC ACIDS

A structure for Deoxyribose Nucleic Acid

We wish to suggest a structure for the salt of deoxyribose nucleic acid (D. N. A.). This structure has novel features which are of considerable biological interest.
A structure for nucleic acid has already been proposed by Pauling and Corey[1]. They kindly made their manuscript available to us in advance of publication. Their model consists of three intertwined chains, with the phosphates near the fibre axis and the bases on the outside. In our opinion, this structure is unsatisfactory for two reasons: (1) We believe that the material which gives the X-ray diagrams is the salt, not the free acid. Without the acidic hydrogen atom, it is not clear what forces would hold the structure together, especially as the negatively charged phosphates near the axis will repel each other. (2) Some of the Van der Waals distances appear to be too small.

Figure 1.1

INTRODUCTION

'Life is the shape it is for a purpose. And when you see how things really are, all the hurt and the waste falls away and what is left is the beauty.'

These words are reputed to have been said by the scientist Rosalind Franklin on seeing for the first time the model shown in the photograph above. Rather an overstatement you might think. After all, it looks just like a few retort stands with clamps holding a variety of bits and pieces together. Perhaps even more difficult to believe is the fact that the two scientists looking at their mangled creation with so much pride were awarded the Nobel prize for their effort!

James Watson and Francis Crick spent many years trying to find out how to build their model which shows the structure of one of the most important molecules known to man - *deoxyribonucleic acid*, or *DNA* for short. The results of their hard work opened the lid to a Pandora's box of further research and has helped us to understand the complexities of inheritance and evolution - the topics that are dealt with in this book. The work carried out by Rosalind Franklin, and her colleague Maurice Wilkins, contributed greatly to finding out the structure of DNA. Sadly she died before the Nobel prize was awarded - this prize of prizes is not awarded posthumously! Wilkins shared the Nobel prize with Watson and Crick.

Watson and Crick published their discovery of the structure of DNA in the Journal *Nature* in 1953. Figure.1.1 shows a section of the actual article which takes up the space of one sheet of A4 - testimony to the fact that it is quality that counts in written work, not quantity!

The magic of DNA lies in the fact that it is the molecule which is responsible for many of the characteristics (i.e. features) shown by living organisms. Some of these characteristics are easy to see such as skin colour or height. Others, for example blood groups, are not so easy to see but their existence cannot be denied. They too have been created by the biochemical behaviour of DNA.

It is DNA, with all its power to determine characteristics, that we inherit from our parents. For this reason, an appreciation of DNA is fundamental to any understanding of *genetics* - a topic which can be defined as *the study of inherited characteristics*.

ROSALIND FRANKLIN (1920 - 1958)

Rosalind Franklin

Rosalind Franklin left school at 18 to study at Cambridge. In 1942 (during the Second World War) she left Cambridge to carry out research into possible new uses of coal. She used X-rays to find out how the atoms in coal were arranged. After the war she spent four further years on this work in Paris. In 1951 she set up an X-ray diffraction unit at King's College, London. It was during her time at King's that she produced the X-ray photographs of DNA which helped Watson and Crick so much.

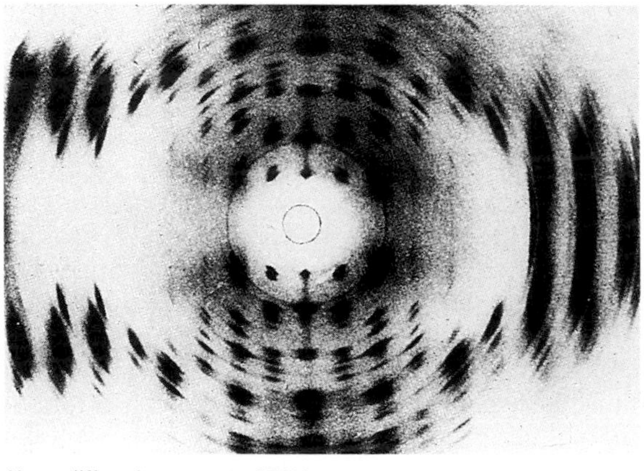

X-ray diffraction pattern of DNA

'CLIMBING' THE LADDER

The first thing to appreciate about DNA is its structure. Imagine a tiny ladder twisted so that it forms a helix or spiral - that is what DNA looks like. Both rails of the ladder are made out of sugar and phosphate molecules stacked one on top of the other in an alternating sequence. The D in DNA is there because the name of the sugar molecule is *deoxyribose*. The rungs of the ladder are made out of nitrogenous bases. DNA has four bases. Two are purines - adenine and guanine, and two are pyrimidines - cytosine and thymine.

Because of the chemical properties of the bases, adenine (A) always pairs up with thymine (T) to form one type of rung, and cytosine (C) always pairs up with guanine (G) to form the other type of rung (see Fig.1.2). The bases are attached to the deoxyribose sugar molecules of the rails and are held together in the middle of the rung by hydrogen bonds. If you look at Fig.1.3(e) you will see a diagram showing the structure of a piece of DNA. Twist this ladder-like structure so that each rail forms a helix and you have the ladder of life - the so called *double helix* (see Fig 1.3(f)).

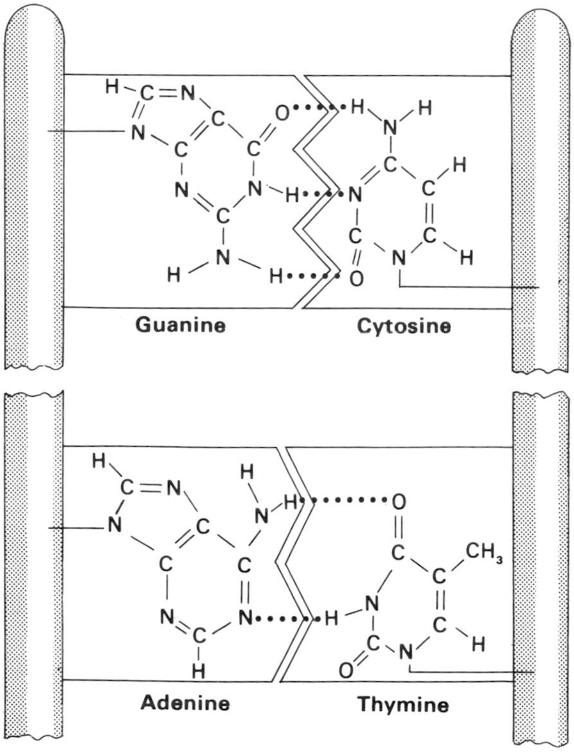
Guanine
Cytosine
Adenine
Thymine

Figure 1.2 Base-pairing in DNA. Note that there are only two types of 'rung' each consisting of one purine and one pyrimidine

Each deoxyribose molecule with its phosphate and base attached forms a molecular threesome called a *nucleotide*. Nucleic acids are built up using these building blocks.

Q How many nucleotides can you recognise in diagram (e) of Fig.1.3?

With the exception of mature red blood cells, DNA is found in every living cell of your body. It resides in the nucleus from where it acts like a biochemical 'Big Brother' controlling what goes on in the rest of the cell. An understanding of this process is the key to seeing how DNA controls the characteristics we inherit.

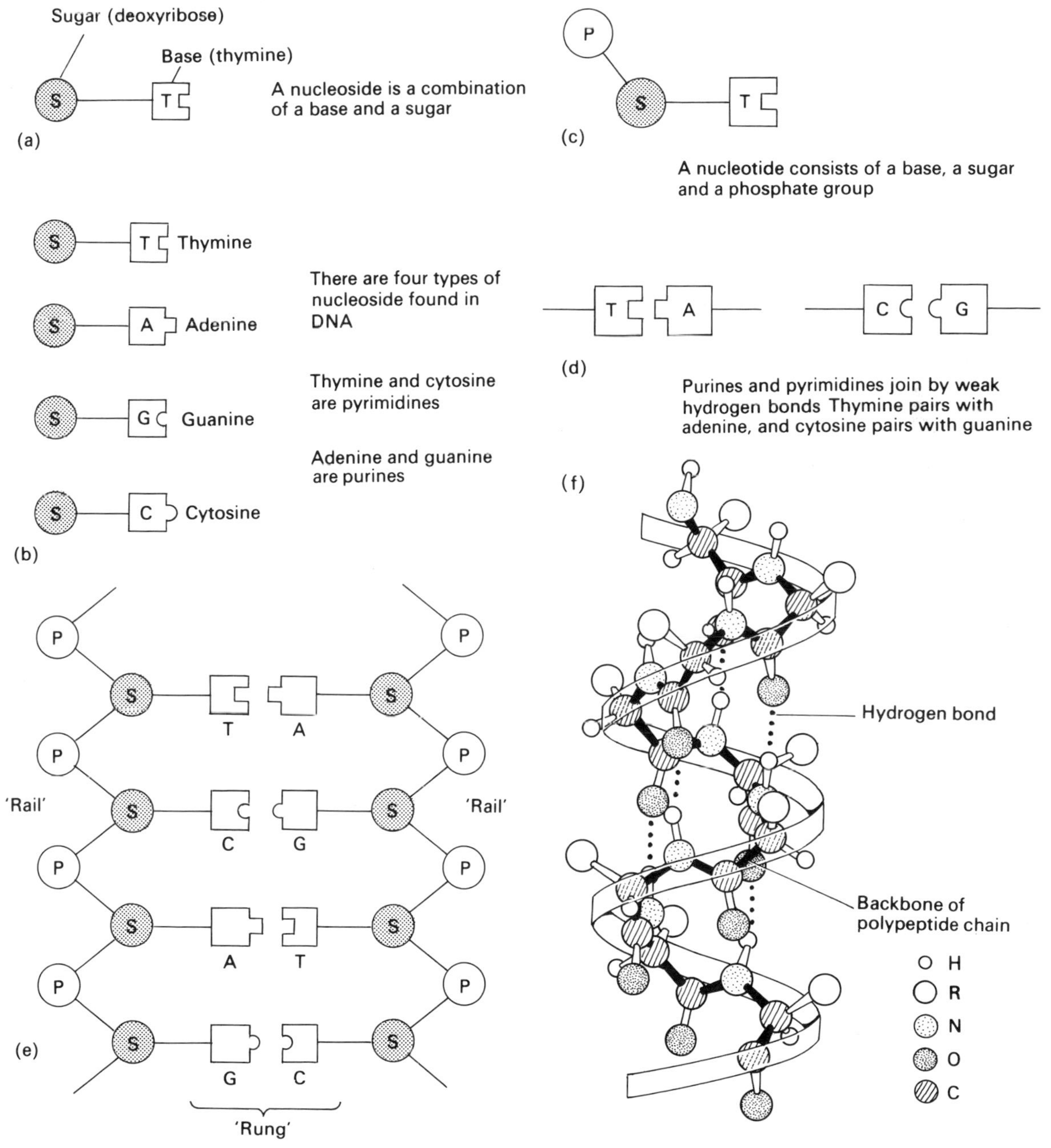

Sugar (deoxyribose)
Base (thymine)
S
T
A nucleoside is a combination of a base and a sugar
(a)
P
S
T
(c)
A nucleotide consists of a base, a sugar and a phosphate group
T Thymine
A Adenine
G Guanine
C Cytosine
(b)
There are four types of nucleoside found in DNA
Thymine and cytosine are pyrimidines
Adenine and guanine are purines
T A
C G
(d)
Purines and pyrimidines join by weak hydrogen bonds Thymine pairs with adenine, and cytosine pairs with guanine
P
S
T A
C G
A T
G C
'Rail'
'Rail'
'Rung'
(e)
(f)
Hydrogen bond
Backbone of polypeptide chain
H
R
N
O
C

Figure 1.3 The ladder-like structure of DNA is a double-stranded molecule with 'rungs' made of paired bases and 'rails' made of sugars and phosphates

THE IMPORTANCE OF ENZYMES

One way in which DNA controls the characteristics we inherit is by helping to make biological catalysts called enzymes. Enzymes are proteins that control the *metabolic* pathways in the body. Metabolism of all of the anabolic (i.e. building up) and catabolic (i.e. breaking down) reactions in the body. To appreciate the role enzymes play in producing characteristics you need only look at the complex metabolic pathways shown in Fig.1.4. These show the metabolism of just one amino acid, tyrosine, in man.

As you can see, you need enzyme A to turn tyrosine into another chemical called dihydroxyphenylalanine. If you lack enzyme A, this reaction cannot occur and it becomes impossible to continue along the metabolic pathway to make the dark pigment melanin. Without melanin your skin will lack pigmentation and you will be an albino with characteristic white hair and pink eyes, a condition known as albinism. So the absence of enzyme A results in a very noticeable change in appearance.

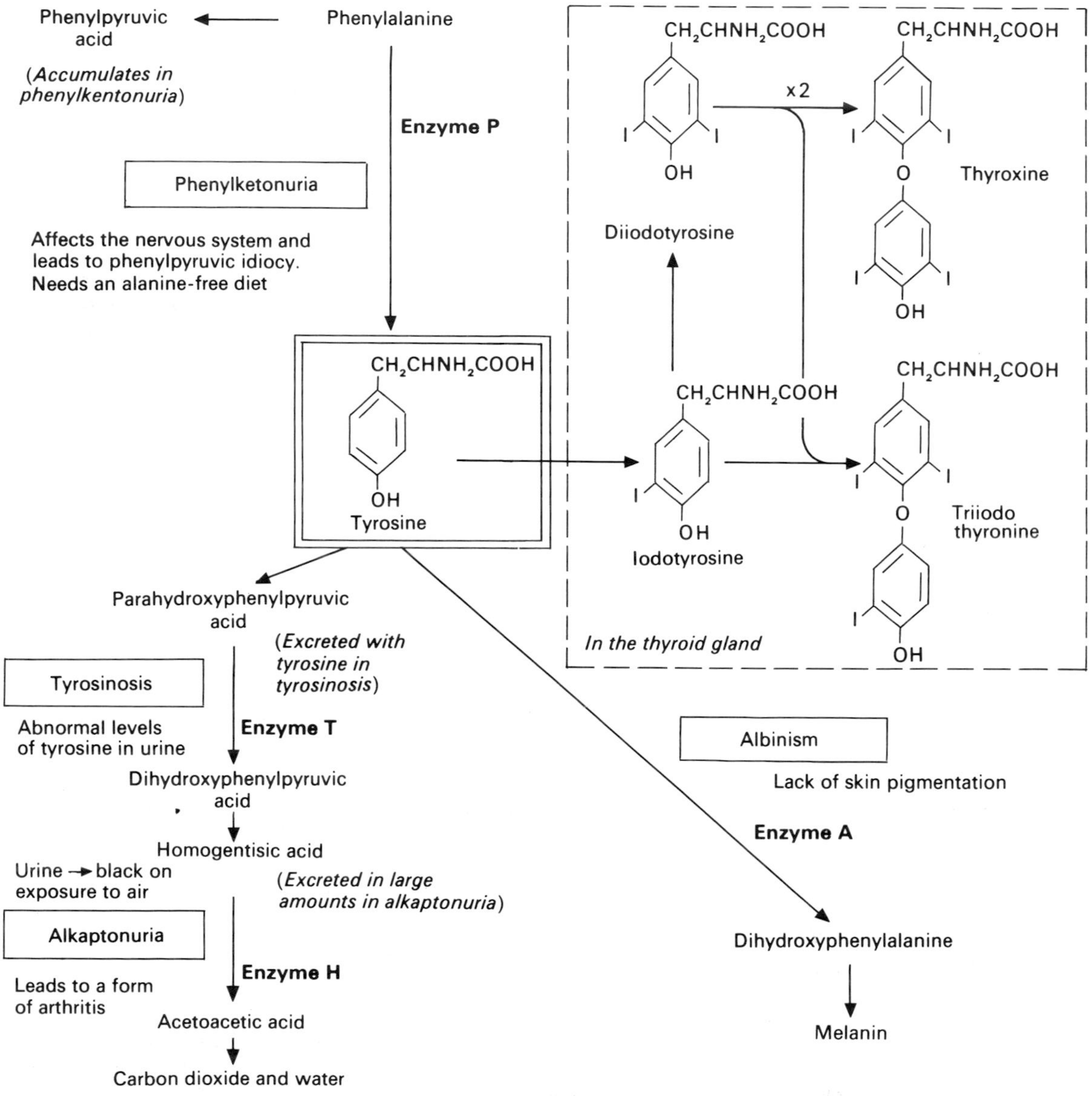

Phenylpyruvic acid
Phenylalanine
(Accumulates in phenylkentonuria)
Enzyme P
Phenylketonuria
Affects the nervous system and leads to phenylpyruvic idiocy. Needs an alanine-free diet
CH2CHNH2COOH
OH
Tyrosine
Diiodotyrosine
x2
Thyroxine
Iodotyrosine
Triiodo thyronine
In the thyroid gland
I
O
Parahydroxyphenylpyruvic acid
(Excreted with tyrosine in tyrosinosis)
Tyrosinosis
Abnormal levels of tyrosine in urine
Enzyme T
Dihydroxyphenylpyruvic acid
Homogentisic acid
Urine → black on exposure to air
(Excreted in large amounts in alkaptonuria)
Alkaptonuria
Leads to a form of arthritis
Enzyme H
Acetoacetic acid
Carbon dioxide and water
Albinism
Lack of skin pigmentation
Enzyme A
Dihydroxyphenylalanine
Melanin

Figure 1.4 Metabolism of tyrosine in man

The disease phenylketonuria is also due to the lack of an enzyme, enzyme P, in an affected individual. Enzyme P helps to convert the amino acid phenylalanine into tyrosine. Failure to do this will allow too much phenylalanine to be free to make phenylpyruvic acid, a chemical which causes damage to the developing nervous system of babies. A sample of blood is always taken from the heel of newborn babies and used to find out what level of phenylalanine it contains. If the level is too high, the baby is put on a diet without the amino acid alanine until its nervous system is fully developed.

Two other enzyme disorders, tyrosinosis and alkaptonuria, are shown in the metabolic pathway of tyrosine (see Fig.1.4). Note that some parts of the pathway have enzyme controlled reactions to manufacture the hormones in the thyroid gland.

So, if enzymes can be made, chemical reactions can take place which give rise to characteristics. The question which must now be answered is 'how is DNA involved in the manufacture of enzymes?'

Enzymes are proteins and like all proteins they are made of amino acids joined together by peptide bonds to form a long chain. The sequence of amino acids can vary due to the fact that the 20 or so known amino acids can be linked together in a number of different ways. Thus a large number of different proteins can be made (see Fig.1.5).

(a)

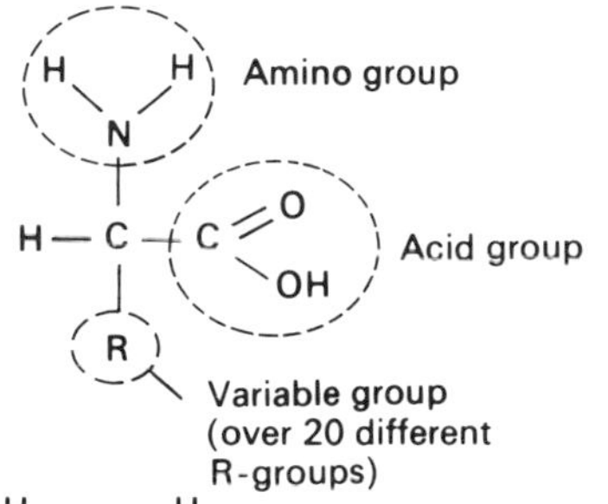
Amino group
Acid group
Variable group
(over 20 different
R-groups)

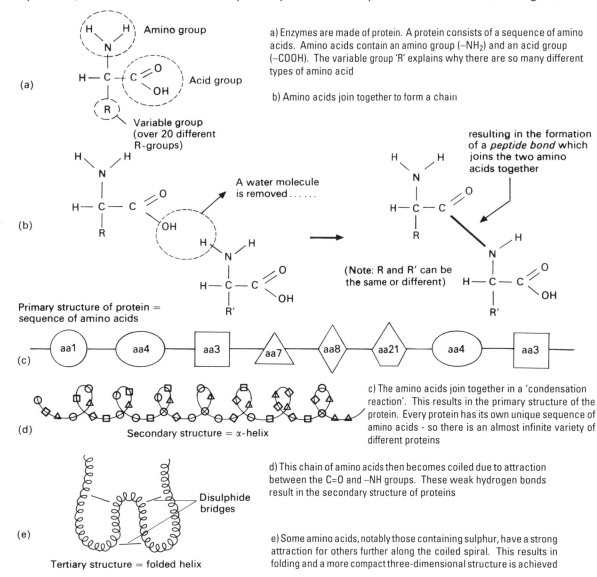

a) Enzymes are made of protein. A protein consists of a sequence of amino acids. Amino acids contain an amino group ($-NH_2$) and an acid group ($-COOH$). The variable group 'R' explains why there are so many different types of amino acid

b) Amino acids join together to form a chain

(b)

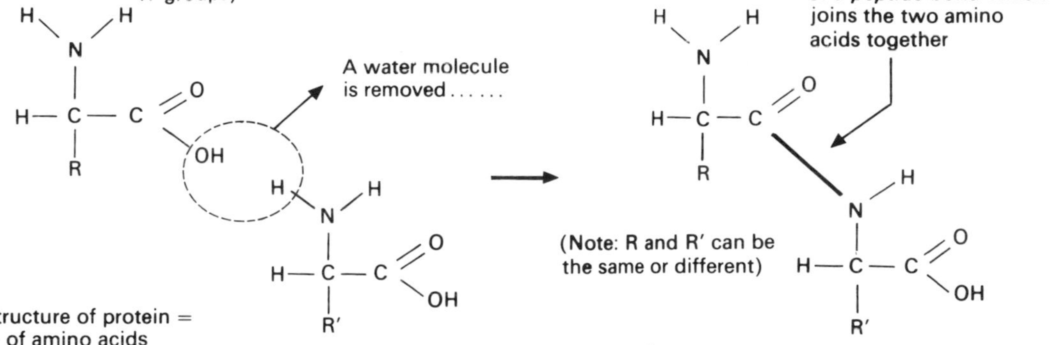
A water molecule
is removed......
resulting in the formation
of a *peptide bond* which
joins the two amino
acids together
(Note: R and R′ can be
the same or different)

(c)

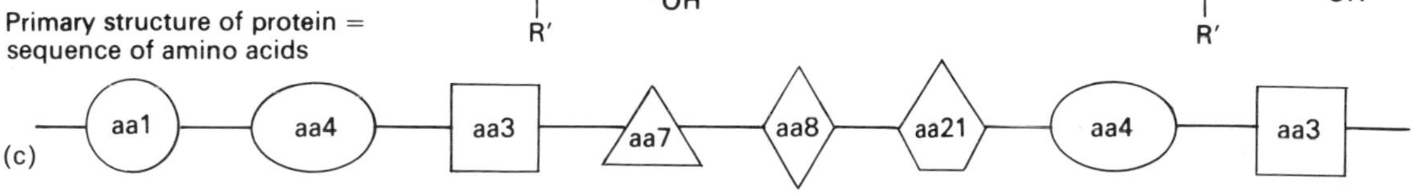
Primary structure of protein =
sequence of amino acids
aa1
aa4
aa3
aa7
aa8
aa21
aa4
aa3

(d)

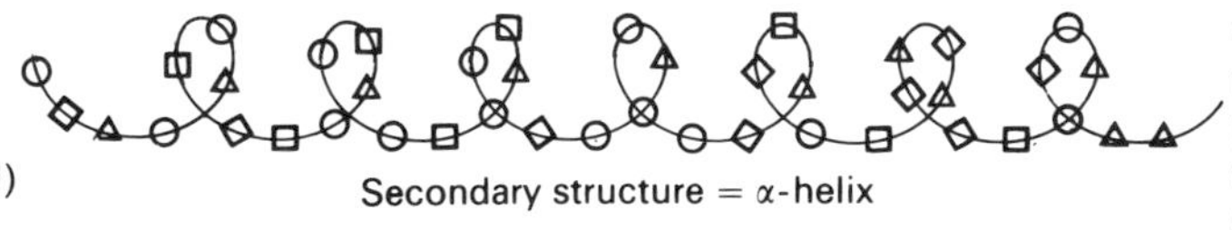
Secondary structure = α-helix

c) The amino acids join together in a 'condensation reaction'. This results in the primary structure of the protein. Every protein has its own unique sequence of amino acids - so there is an almost infinite variety of different proteins

d) This chain of amino acids then becomes coiled due to attraction between the C=O and –NH groups. These weak hydrogen bonds result in the secondary structure of proteins

(e)

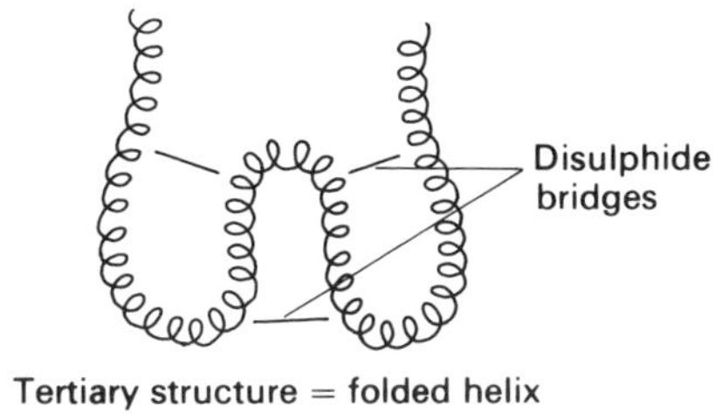
Disulphide
bridges
Tertiary structure = folded helix

e) Some amino acids, notably those containing sulphur, have a strong attraction for others further along the coiled spiral. This results in folding and a more compact three-dimensional structure is achieved

Figure 1.5 Enzyme structure

The particular sequence of amino acids in an enzyme molecule, or any protein for that matter, is very important. This is because certain amino acids in the chain are attracted to each other and this attraction tends to fold the chain up into a three-dimensional (3-D) shape. This 3-D shape gives rise to the active sites (see Fig.1.6) of enzymes and is also important in enabling non-enzymic proteins to carry out their functions. Enzymes catalyse specific reactions. Some enzymes work on only one chemical (i.e. substrate specific), other enzymes can catalyse a group of related reactions. Indeed, the specificity of enzymes owes itself to the fact that different amino acid sequences provide opportunities for different patterns of folding and hence different shaped active sites. The diagrams in Fig.1.6 help to show this point.

(a)

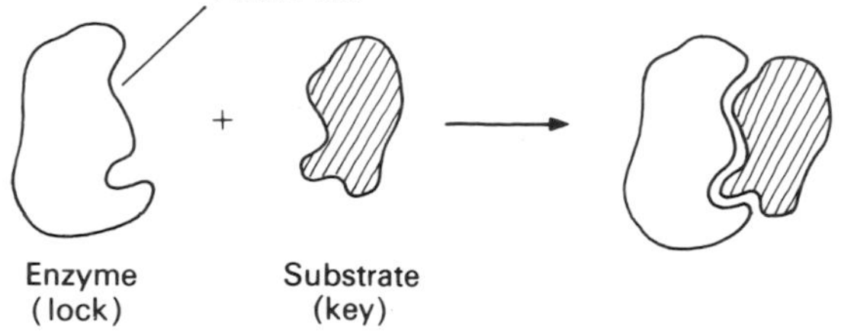

Active site
+
Enzyme
(lock)
Substrate
(key)

Enzymes have specific areas called active sites which recognise and bind to the substrate. An enzyme-substrate is formed when the enzyme and substrate bind together successfully. Changes in the enzyme's shape (e.g. due to heat, pH and certain chemical inhibitors) can alter the shape of the active site rendering the enzyme inactive

(b)

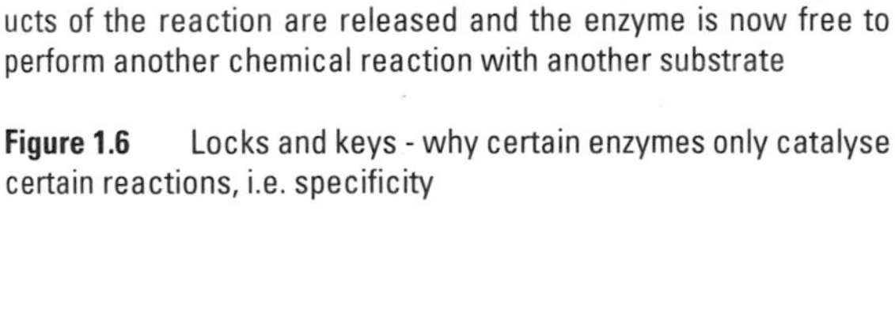

S2
S1
+
+
S1
S2
Enzyme

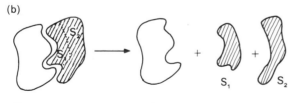

The substrate is broken down to produce two products. The products of the reaction are released and the enzyme is now free to perform another chemical reaction with another substrate

Figure 1.6 Locks and keys - why certain enzymes only catalyse certain reactions, i.e. specificity

UNFOLDING THE MESSAGE

To begin the process of protein synthesis a piece of the double-stranded DNA ladder 'unzips' itself along the middle of the rungs. Only one of the single strands produced is used in the next stage where an enzyme called *ribonucleic acid polymerase* plays an important role. This enzyme encourages the manufacture of a nucleic acid called *messenger RNA (mRNA)*. *RNA*, or *ribonucleic acid*, is different in three main ways from DNA. Firstly, it is single stranded. Secondly, it uses the sugar *ribose* instead of deoxyribose and, finally, the base thymine is replaced by uracil (U).

The 'unzipped' DNA provides a single strand which acts as a template for pairing up with complimentary bases (i.e. A with T; C with G; G with C and U with A) when given catalytic encouragement from ribonucleic acid polymerase. The product is mRNA and the process, called *transcription*, occurs in the cell nucleus.

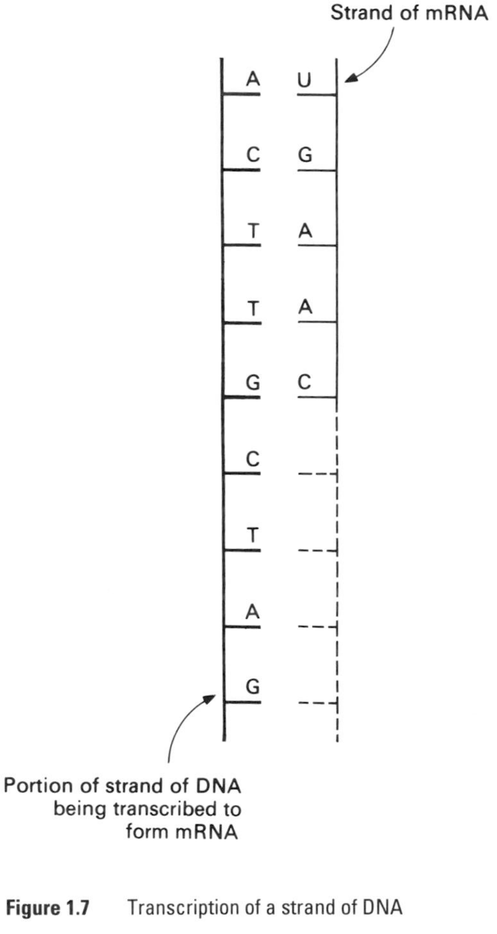

Strand of mRNA
A U
C G
T A
T A
G C
C
T
A
G
Portion of strand of DNA
being transcribed to
form mRNA

Figure 1.7 Transcription of a strand of DNA

Figure 1.7 shows a strand of DNA being transcribed. The mRNA produced depends on the type and sequence of bases in the DNA. Note that in mRNA the base thymine is replaced with uracil.

Q Complete the sequence of bases on the mRNA molecule shown by the dotted line in Fig.1.7.

The newly created mRNA passes through pores in the nuclear membrane into the cytoplasm. In effect a message (hence the name messenger RNA) has been sent to the cytoplasm. The message is in code, the genetic code, and the metabolic machinery of the cytoplasm now needs to decode the message.

TRANSLATING THE MESSAGE

In the cytoplasm there are two other types of RNA. One of them is called *ribosomal RNA (rRNA)* and the other is called *transfer RNA (tRNA)*. On passing into the cytoplasm the mRNA moves to a *ribosome* and links with its rRNA in a way which helps to expose the code of the messenger RNA to the cytoplasm. Ribosomes act as sites of protein synthesis in the cell. They provide a sheltered site where tRNA conveys amino acids to the mRNA for the production of polypeptide chains.

The tRNA, like mRNA, is single stranded but it is coiled up in a three-dimensional arrangement which is shaped rather like a clover leaf (see Fig.1.8). By coiling up on itself the tRNA leaves three bases exposed. Many molecules of tRNA exist in the cytoplasm, each with a different combination of three exposed bases. Attached to each different tRNA is a specific amino acid. Transfer RNAs therefore can differ in the type of bases exposed and in the specific amino acid attached.

The three exposed bases of a tRNA molecule are called an *anticodon*. They will be attracted to the three bases on the mRNA molecule to which they are complimentary. This complimentary triplet of bases on the mRNA is called a *codon*. Anticodons are brought into contact with codons when rRNA slides along a mRNA molecule. In this way, amino acids attached to tRNAs are brought close together and a peptide bond can be formed. Once a tRNA has released its amino acid it returns to the cytoplasm to find another amino acid of the same type.

As the process continues along the entire length of a mRNA molecule a chain of amino acids is created and a polypeptide is born. The coded message of the mRNA has now been translated into another language, a sequence of amino acids or the language of proteins. It comes as no surprise to learn that this stage of the process is called *translation*. This important sequence is illustrated in Fig.1.9.

Transcription and translation ensure that the sequence of bases in DNA determines the sequence of amino acids in a polypeptide which in turn determines the shape of the polypeptide and therefore its ability to work. Remember that some polypeptides become structural proteins and others become enzymes.

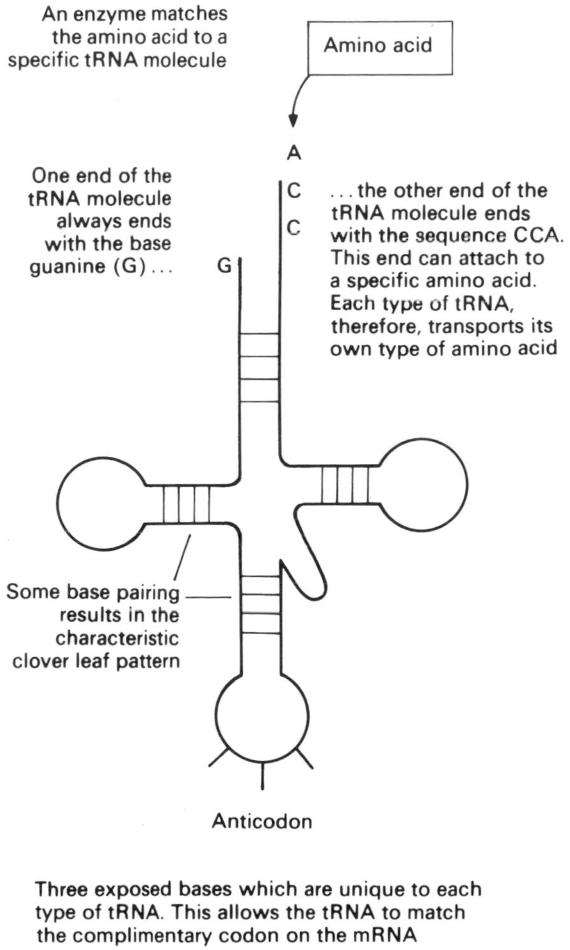

An enzyme matches the amino acid to a specific tRNA molecule
Amino acid
A
C
C
One end of the tRNA molecule always ends with the base guanine (G) ...
G
... the other end of the tRNA molecule ends with the sequence CCA. This end can attach to a specific amino acid. Each type of tRNA, therefore, transports its own type of amino acid
Some base pairing results in the characteristic clover leaf pattern
Anticodon
Three exposed bases which are unique to each type of tRNA. This allows the tRNA to match the complimentary codon on the mRNA

Figure 1.8 Clover leaf pattern of tRNA

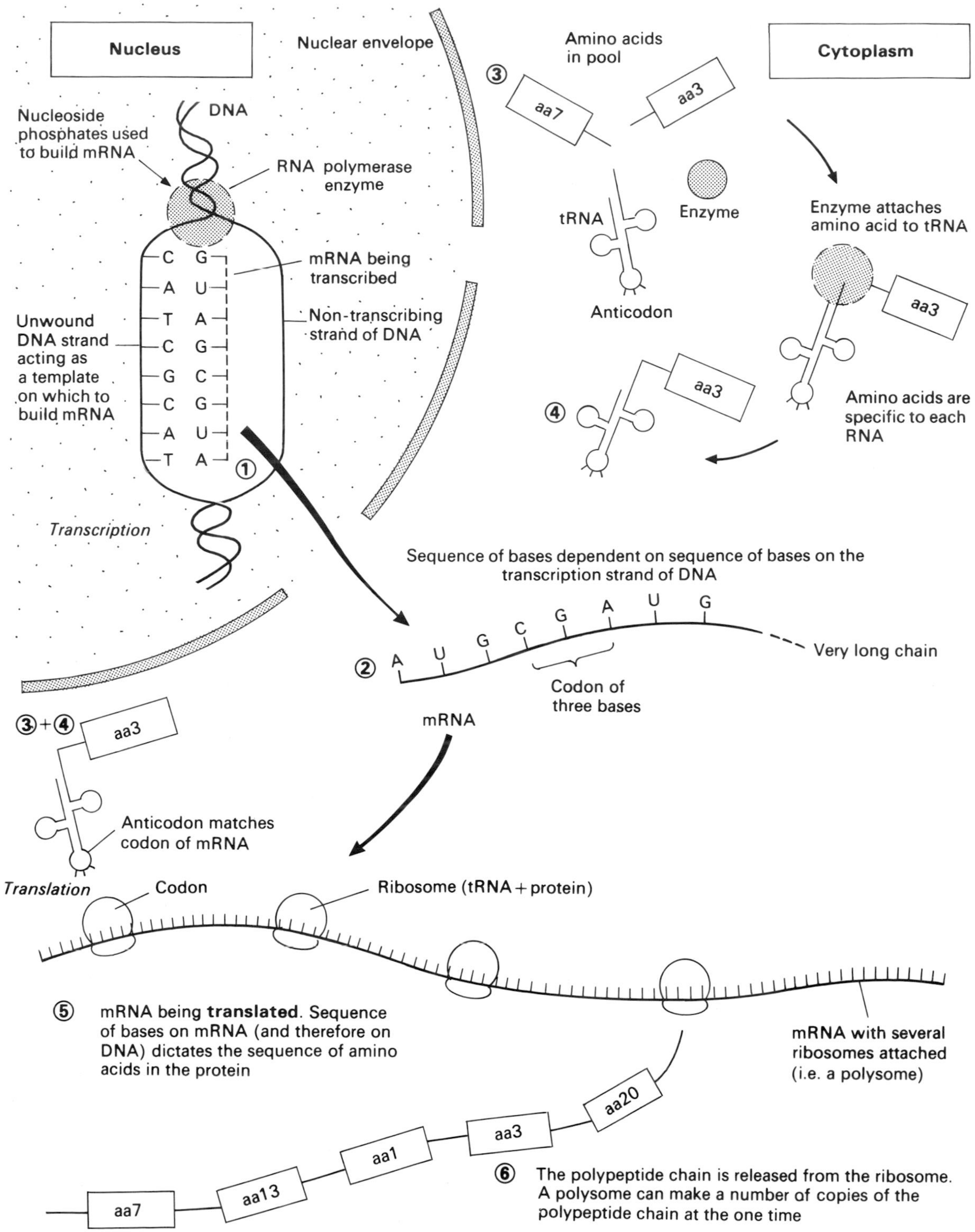
Nucleus
Nuclear envelope
Nucleoside phosphates used to build mRNA
DNA
RNA polymerase enzyme
C G
A U
T A
C G
G C
C G
A U
T A
mRNA being transcribed
Non-transcribing strand of DNA
Unwound DNA strand acting as a template on which to build mRNA
①
Transcription
③
Amino acids in pool
aa7
aa3
Cytoplasm
tRNA
Enzyme
Anticodon
Enzyme attaches amino acid to tRNA
aa3
④
aa3
Amino acids are specific to each RNA
Sequence of bases dependent on sequence of bases on the transcription strand of DNA
② A U G C G A U G
Very long chain
Codon of three bases
mRNA
③+④
aa3
Anticodon matches codon of mRNA
Translation
Codon
Ribosome (tRNA + protein)
⑤ mRNA being **translated**. Sequence of bases on mRNA (and therefore on DNA) dictates the sequence of amino acids in the protein
mRNA with several ribosomes attached (i.e. a polysome)
aa20
aa3
aa1
aa13
aa7
⑥ The polypeptide chain is released from the ribosome. A polysome can make a number of copies of the polypeptide chain at the one time

Figure 1.9 Events leading to the synthesis of a polypeptide. At stage 2, the sequence of bases on the mRNA depends on the sequence of bases on the template strand of DNA. At stage 6, the nature of the protein is determined by the polypeptide chain, which in turn reflects the original sequence of bases on the template strand of DNA

WHEN THINGS GO WRONG!

There are times when the sequence of bases in a DNA molecule is altered. Random changes in the base sequence of DNA are called mutations. Mutations are rare, random changes in the genetic material but there are many factors which can increase the rate at which they occur. Such factors are called mutagens and examples include radioactivity, X-rays, mustard gas, uv light, hydrogen peroxide, and the drug thalidomide. Mutations can change the type of proteins being made by a cell and this can be a severe problem for an individual. Albinism, phenylketonuria, tyrosinosis and alkaptonuria are all enzyme disorders which are the result of a mutation. In each of these cases the type of protein (i.e. enzyme) being made is unable to function correctly.

To understand how mutations can change the type of protein produced, you need to remember that each set of three nucleotides in mRNA is translated into a specific amino acid according to the rules shown in Fig.1.9. The three nucleotides are said to act as *genetic code* for a particular amino acid. For example, using the genetic code in Table 1.1, one codon for the amino acid methionine is AUG. What happens if a mutation occurs? Sometimes just one base in a codon is changed (e.g. AUG to AUU) but often a mutation may involve the insertion of an additional base into the mRNA during transcription, or sometimes a base is left out. The effect of either of these latter two events is to change the sequence of codons and hence the amino acids so that a different polypeptide is formed by that mRNA molecule.

Use Table 1.1 to answer the following question.

An amino acid sequence has the following sequence of codons:

AUG CCA UAC GGU UGG AAG

1. What are the amino acids in this sequence?

2. What would happen to the amino acid sequence if the following mutations occured?
AUC CCA UAC GAU UGG AAG

First position	Second position				Third position
	U	C	A	G	
U	phe	ser	tyr	cys	U
	phe	ser	tyr	cys	C
	leu	ser	Stop	Stop	A
	leu	ser	Stop	trp	G
C	leu	pro	his	arg	U
	leu	pro	his	arg	C
	leu	pro	gln	arg	A
	leu	pro	gln	arg	G
A	ile	thr	asn	ser	U
	ile	thr	asn	ser	C
	ile	thr	lys	arg	A
	met	thr	lys	arg	G
G	val	ala	asp	gly	U
	val	ala	asp	gly	C
	val	ala	glu	gly	A
	val	ala	glu	gly	G

Table 1.1 The genetic code: the codons on mRNA and the amino acids (shown as abbreviations) that they code for: phe = phenylalanine, leu = leucine, ile = isoleucine, val = valine, ser = serine, pro = proline, thr = threonine, ala = alanine, tyr = tyrosine, his = histidine, gln = glutamine, asn = asparagine, lys = lysine, asp = aspartate, glu = glutamate, cys = cysteine, trp = tryptophan, arg = arginine, gly = glycine

Not all characteristics are determined by enzyme-controlled chemical reactions. For example, the oxygen carrying pigment, haemoglobin, only functions correctly if its four polypeptide chains are folded in the right way. Once again, the sequence of amino acids in these polypeptide chains is determined by the sequence of bases in the DNA.

In a disorder called sickle cell anaemia the red blood cells become distorted and tend to rupture long before the 120 days they should normally survive. No wonder then that sufferers of this disease are victims of an unpleasant and often fatal anaemia. This blood disorder is caused by a mutation which results in the amino acid valine being substituted for the normal amino acid glutamic acid at one place on one of the polypeptide chains (see Fig.1.10).

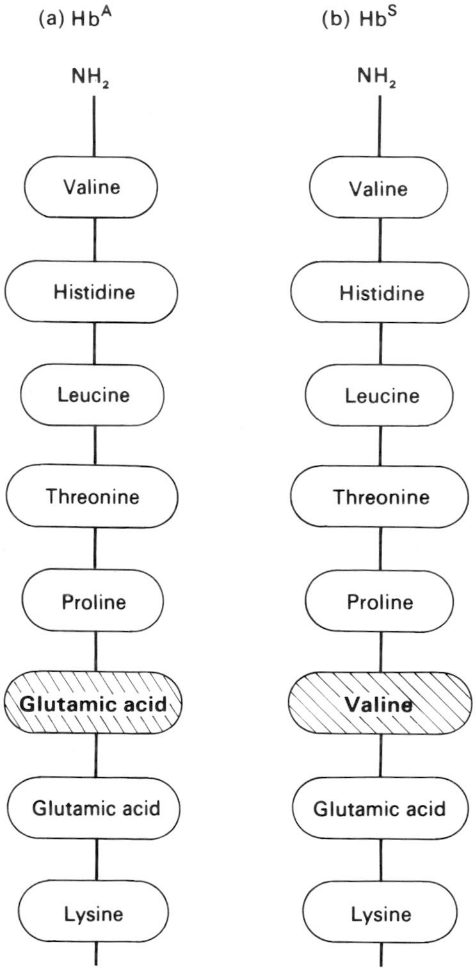

(a) Hb^A
NH2
Valine
Histidine
Leucine
Threonine
Proline
Glutamic acid
Glutamic acid
Lysine
(b) Hb^S
NH2
Valine
Histidine
Leucine
Threonine
Proline
Valine
Glutamic acid
Lysine

Figure 1.10 N–terminal portions of (a) normal haemoglobin (Hb^A) and (b) sickle cell haemoglobin (Hb^S)

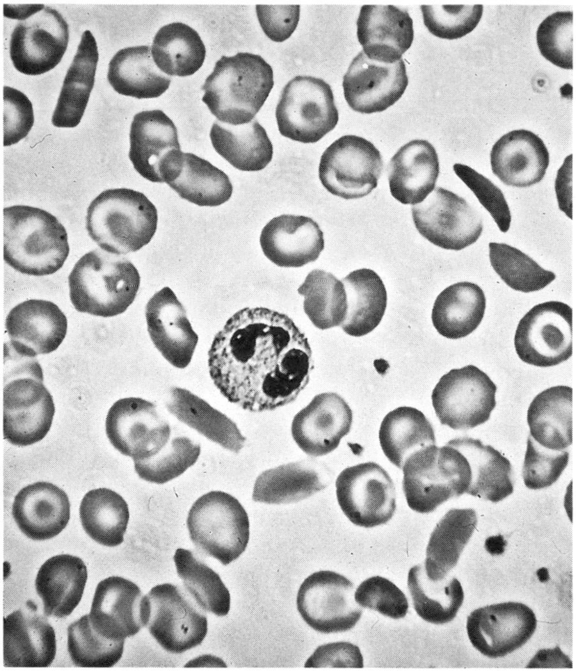

Normal and sickle-celled red blood cells

Q Look carefully at the photograph above. Can you identify the normal red blood cells and the sickle cells?

GENES AND CHROMOSOMES

The part of DNA which is used to make a polypeptide is called a *gene*. A gene is a specific length of a DNA molecule made up of a sequence of nucleotides to which a specific function can be assigned. DNA will consist of many different genes, each responsible for making a different protein. Together, these genes are responsible for making you look like you do. They control the creation of your characteristics. There are a number of different lengths of DNA found in the nuclei of organisms. Each length consists of genes and is called a *chromosome*.

■ MUTATIONS

One of the features of cell division and DNA replication is that the daughter cells need to inherit a full set of genetic instructions from the parent cell (unless the daughter cell is destined to be a sex cell, i.e. a gamete). There are instances, however, where things do go wrong and a faulty or incomplete message is passed on. Such an unpredictable and spontaneous change is referred to as a *mutation*. Mutations can occur in different ways and can be sparked off by environmental influences.

A mutation can be defined as an inherited change in the genetic information of a cell, and cells with this altered information are called *mutants*. Ultraviolet, cosmic, alpha, beta and X-ray radiation and some chemicals such as colchicine, thalidomide, mustard gas, cigarette smoke and even caffeine are able to bring about genetic changes and are described as *mutagens*.

Gene mutations (or point mutations) involve a change in the sequence of bases in the DNA molecule. If one of the bases is lost or duplicated or has another base substituted for it, it may change the amino acid sequence in the protein for which that section of DNA codes. Changes in the amino acid sequence of the protein may affect its biological efficiency as is the case in sickle cell anaemia (see page 10). Although only one amino acid (valine for glutamic acid) is altered out of 146 in the beta polypeptide chain of the haemoglobin molecule, it causes the molecule to crystallise in low oxygen concentrations. As a result, the altered molecule cannot transport oxygen as efficiently and this can lead to complications such as muscular pains, and heart and kidney failure.

Chromosomal mutations can involve the loss or gain of a single chromosome (this is called *aneuploidy*), due to non-disjunction at cell division or an increase in an entire set of chromosomes (a condition known as *polyploidy*). Down's syndrome (see page 54) is a well known example of aneuploidy where the affected individual has one extra of chromosome 21. Polyploidy is quite widespread amongst plants (ferns are highly polyploid and this might explain their rather slow evolution). The number of chromosomes in a gamete is described as 'n'. In humans, n=23. Body (somatic) cells have 2n chromosomes and are termed diploid (i.e. they have two sets of chromosomes, one from each parent). *Autopolyploidy* arises when the cytoplasm fails to divide leaving a cell with 4n chromosomes. Autopolyploid plants are usually fertile and display increased vigour. Many of our important food crops, e.g. sugar beet, tomatoes and tobacco are polyploids. *Allopolyploids* arise when a sterile hybrid spontaneously doubles its chromosome number enabling it to become fertile. Modern bread wheats have developed from hybrids between Emmer wheat and wild grasses which have subsequently undergone chromosomal duplication. In addition to these chromosomal changes there are other mutations which involve the loss of, or the duplication of short sections of chromosome during cell division.

Although any cell can mutate at the time of division, those mutations which occur in the production of gametes are significant because all of the resulting cells of the new organism will have the mutation. When body cells (somatic cells) mutate it may be very significant to the individual (e.g. skin cells may mutate as a result of high uv light exposure and develop into tumours), but will be of no genetic significance because the mutation will not be inherited.

Generally, mutations are seen to be disadvantageous but, once in a while, the change conveys some advantage to the mutant. This was the case of the peppered moth (*Biston betularia*) where a darker 'melanic' form became more successful in the polluted areas around industrial towns (see page 90). Although humans have exploited mutations to produce 'fancy' varieties of plants and animals, spontaneous mutation has also been one of the important features behind the whole process of evolution.

JUST WHY WERE WATSON AND CRICK WORKING ON DNA?

Very few scientific discoveries come just 'out of the blue'. Progress is usually made in a series of steps, sometimes a vital connection is drawn and a 'breakthrough' happens. Watson and Crick certainly made the breakthrough... but what of the work that went before?

The discovery of nucleic acids

Nucleic acids were discovered by Miescher in 1897 but the significance of these substances was not appreciated at the time. It was another thirty years before F. Griffith took things a step further.

Griffith was working with the bacterium *Streptococcus pneumonii* which causes pneumonia. This bacterium has two different *phenotypes* (it can exist in two forms) called 'rough' and 'smooth'. The smooth pneumococcus is said to be virulent (meaning that it causes serious and often fatal illnesses) and has a coating made of a polysaccharide carbohydrate. This coating has minor variations which can be detected chemically and these differences are used to identify and classify the smooth types.

Griffith discovered that the variations in coating were inherited in a predictable way. He found that the non-virulent rough pneumococci (termed R) almost always gave rise to other rough pneumococci. However, very rarely, a rough pneumococcus would produce a pneumococcus with a smooth coat. This smooth-coated mutant (called type IIS) then continued to produce smooth-coated pneumococci (although about 1 in 10 million offspring reverted to the original R type). It was apparent that the type R and type IIS pneumococci had two genetically different forms. Griffith also identified another smooth pneumococcus with a different genetic makeup to the other smooth types which he called type IIIS. Griffith set up an experiment using type IIIS pneumococci together with type IIR pneumococci which he had derived from one of the changed type IIS strains (see Fig.1.11).

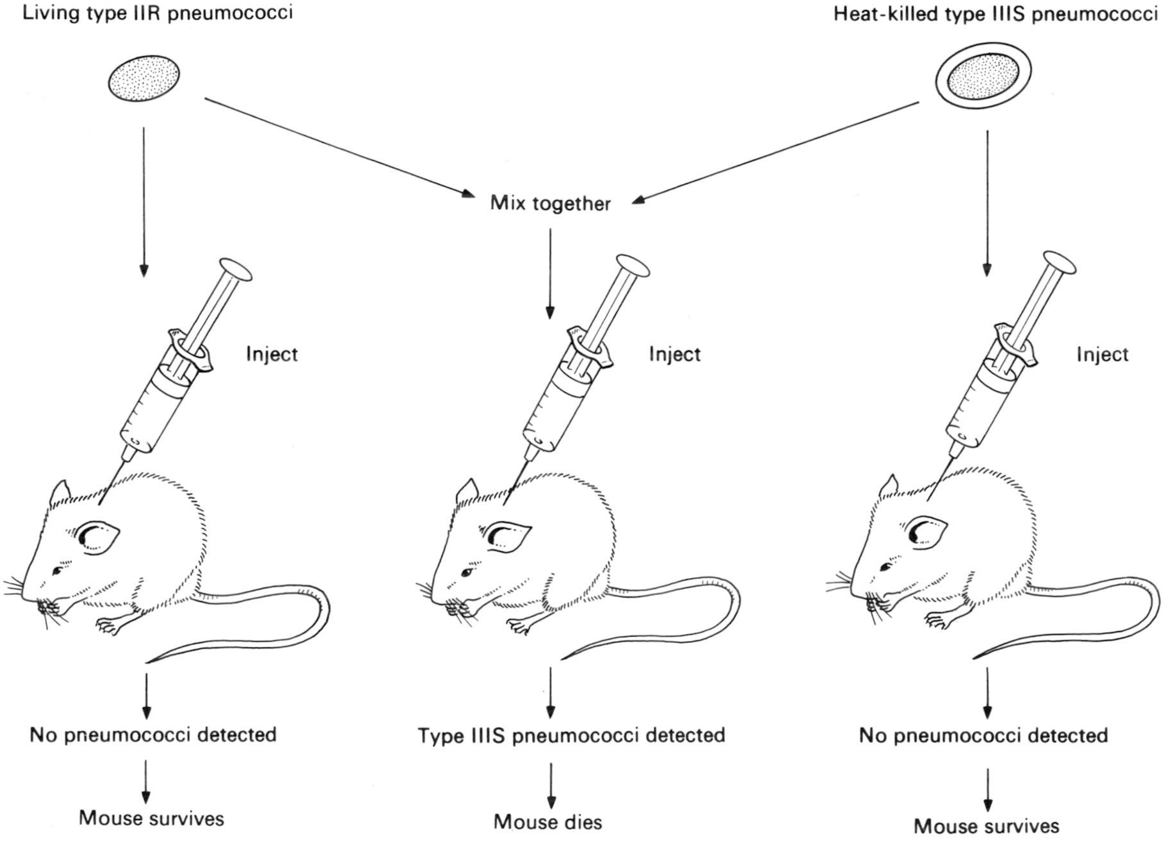

Living type IIR pneumococci
Heat-killed type IIIS pneumococci
Mix together
Inject
Inject
Inject
No pneumococci detected
Type IIIS pneumococci detected
No pneumococci detected
Mouse survives
Mouse dies
Mouse survives

Figure 1.11 Griffith's experiment using mice (i.e. *in vivo*)

The rough and the smooth

Griffith injected a group of mice with a combination of living, non-virulent type IIR pneumococci and heat-killed type IIIS pneumococci (see Fig. 1.11). Normally, the mice would be expected to recover from this treatment but many mice died of pneumonia. When Griffith examined the blood of the dead mice, he found large numbers of living type IIIS pneumococci. Since the living type IIR pneumococci had come from a type IIS strain, the appearance of the IIIS strain could not be explained by a back mutation of the type IIR strain. In some way, the type R pneumococci had been 'transformed' into type IIIS. These new type IIIS pneumococci obtained from the mice continued to produce smooth-coated offspring – in fact, the new instruction had been incorporated into these bacteria.

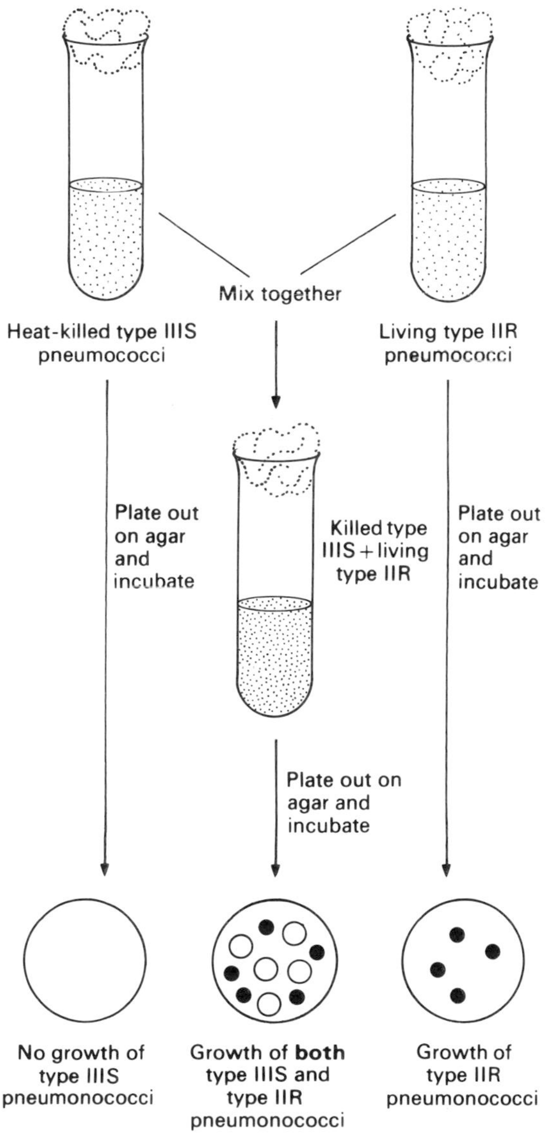
Mix together
Heat-killed type IIIS pneumococci
Living type IIR pneumococci
Plate out on agar and incubate
Killed type IIIS + living type IIR
Plate out on agar and incubate
Plate out on agar and incubate
No growth of type IIIS pneumonococci
Growth of **both** type IIIS and type IIR pneumonococci
Growth of type IIR pneumonococci

Figure 1.12 Griffith's experiment using test tubes (i.e. *in vitro*)

Further experiments showed that this change could be brought about 'in vitro' thus making the investigation somewhat easier. Living type IIR pneumococci could be transformed by growing them in the presence of heat-killed type IIIS pneumococci. But more importantly, extracts from cultures of type IIIS pneumococci also transformed the type R pneumococci (see Fig. 1.12).

The next step should seem obvious! If you can change the nature of a bacterium in this way, then the extract must contain a vital ingredient. It became a challenge to discover the nature of what came to be known as the 'transforming principle' and the hunt was on!

Identifying the 'transforming principle'

In 1944, three scientists O.T. Avery, C.M. McLeod and M. McCarty found the answer. They made extracts of the killed type IIIS pneumonococci and tried separating them into fractions. Eventually they found that the highly purified DNA extracts of the type IIIS pneumonococci could bring about the transformation. Clearly the gross structure of the DNA was the vital 'transforming principle'. If the DNA was broken down by the enzyme DNAase, any kind of 'transforming message' was lost.

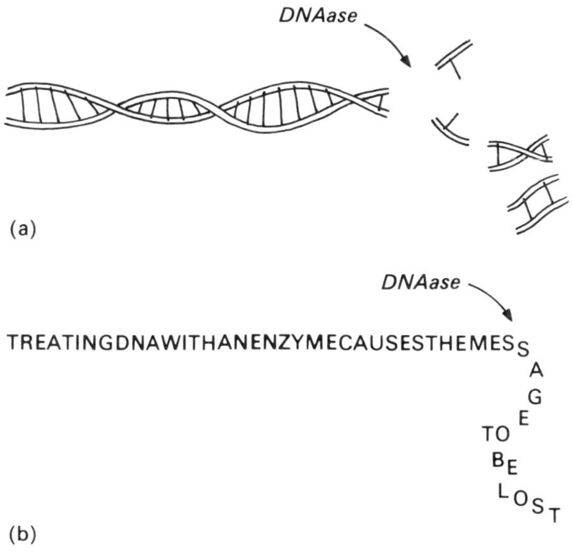
DNAase
(a)
DNAase
TREATINGDNAWITHANENZYMECAUSESTHEMESSAGE TO BE LOST
(b)

Figure 1.13

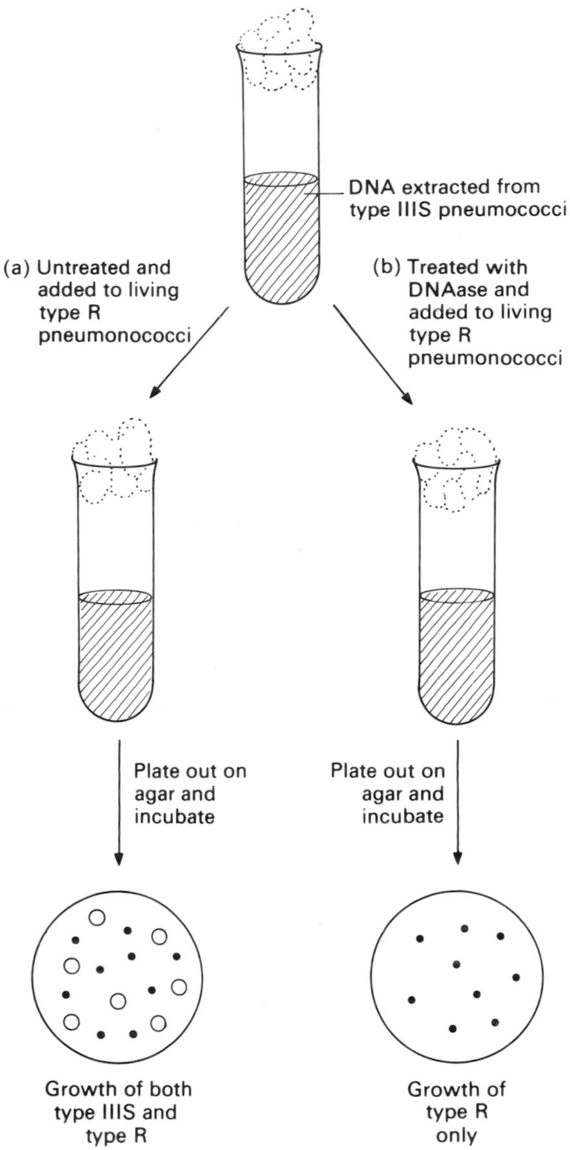
DNA extracted from type IIIS pneumococci
(a) Untreated and added to living type R pneumonococci
(b) Treated with DNAase and added to living type R pneumonococci
Plate out on agar and incubate
Plate out on agar and incubate
Growth of both type IIIS and type R
Growth of type R only

Figure 1.14 The transforming principle

This transformation of bacteria has been demonstrated many times and the changes induced by the DNA are inherited by the transformed organisms and their subsequent offspring.

Griffith, Avery, MacLeod and McCarty had directed research towards DNA – transformation was a fact but the precise mechanism was not established. Certainly, there was much more work to be done. DNA was thought to be the transforming principle but it seemed to lack the variation of other large molecules such as proteins. However, an elegant experiment by Alfred Hershey and Martha Chase would set the DNA trail alight once more.

Phage injects more evidence for DNA!

Hershey and Chase enlisted the help of a simple virus to settle the DNA issue. Most viruses consist of little more than a package of DNA conveniently wrapped up in a protein coat (see Fig. 1.15). A virus which attacks a bacterium is called a *bacteriophage* (or phage). It attaches itself to a bacterium, enters it and finally takes over the bacterium's resources to make copies of itself.

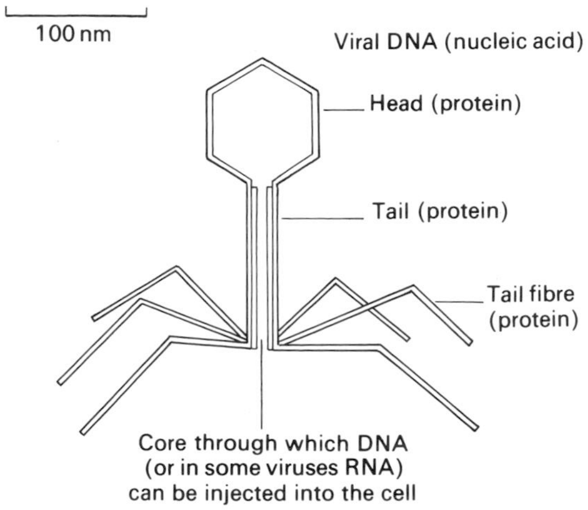
100 nm
Viral DNA (nucleic acid)
Head (protein)
Tail (protein)
Tail fibre (protein)
Core through which DNA (or in some viruses RNA) can be injected into the cell

Figure 1.15 A bacteriophage

The virus is released from the bacterium during *lysis* (cell rupture) and goes on to invade other bacteria. The emerging phage is identical to the original one which invaded the bacterium. Since a virus consists of only two types of molecule, the issue was whether it was the phage protein or the phage DNA which coded for the production of more virus particles.

Host bacteria were cultured in media (i.e. nutrients) containing either radioactive sulphur (^{35}S) or radioactive phosphorus (^{32}P). These radioactive substances are used by the bacteria in exactly the same way as the non-radioactive forms but have the advantage of being capable of being traced as they are used. These substances are known as *tracers* and the chemicals containing them are described as being *labelled* (see Fig. 1.16).

Bacteria fed with radioactive sulphur will have ^{35}S-labelled proteins in their protoplasm whereas those fed on radioactive phosphorus will have ^{32}P-labelled DNA. These two labelled cultures of bacteria were then infected with phage. The phage went on to replicate inside the bacteria and eventually caused them to lyse releasing large numbers of virus. You might like to consider what you think would happen before you read the next paragraph.

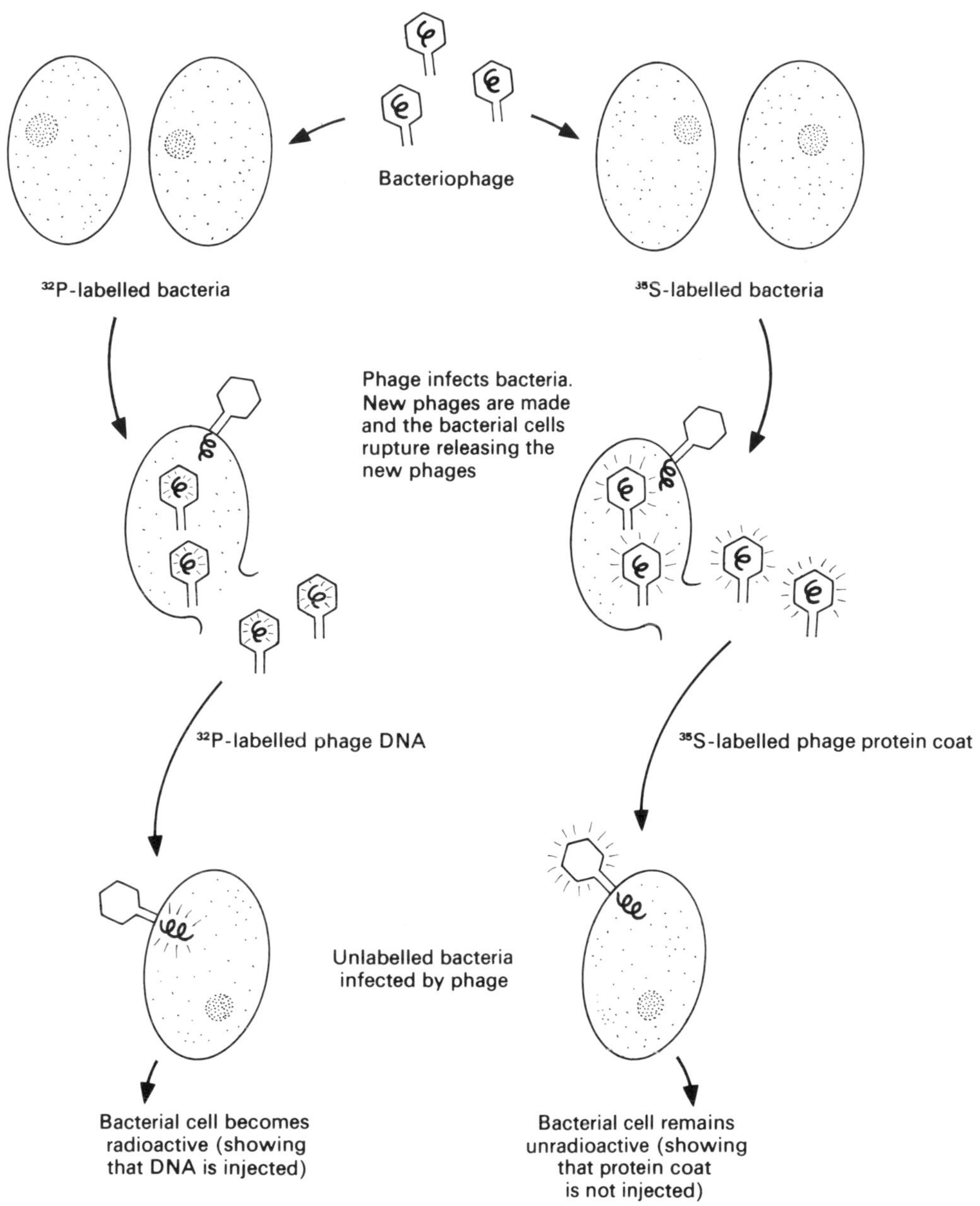
Bacteriophage
³²P-labelled bacteria
³⁵S-labelled bacteria
Phage infects bacteria. New phages are made and the bacterial cells rupture releasing the new phages
³²P-labelled phage DNA
³⁵S-labelled phage protein coat
Unlabelled bacteria infected by phage
Bacterial cell becomes radioactive (showing that DNA is injected)
Bacterial cell remains unradioactive (showing that protein coat is not injected)

Figure 1.16 Hershey and Chase's experiment

Phage particles released from the ^{35}S-labelled bacteria had labelled coats whereas those released from the ^{32}P-labelled bacteria had labelled DNA. The two types of labelled phage were then allowed to infect unlabelled bacteria. The idea was to follow the fate of the phage coat (i.e. protein) and the phage DNA.

Hershey and Chase discovered that the bacteria infected with phage whose coat had been labelled with ^{35}S did *not* become labelled. The protein coat of the phage clearly remained on the *outside* of the bacterium and did not influence the production of new phage particles. On the other hand, the ^{32}P-labelled phage injected its DNA into the bacterium making the bacterial DNA radioactive and at the same time passing on the instruction to make more copies of the phage. Surely then DNA must be the 'stuff of inheritance'!

It should come as no surprise to you that many scientists were now hot on the trail of DNA and that Watson and Crick were in the right place at the right time!

GETTING THE MESSAGE!

All cells contain DNA, the chemical blueprint needed to organise and run the activities of the cell. This DNA resides in the nucleus but many of the cell's activities take place some distance away in the cytoplasm. Evidence for how the message contained in the sequence of bases in the DNA is passed into the protein synthesising factory of the cytoplasm comes from a small organism called *Acetabularia* (see Fig.1.17).

Acetabularia is a simple one-celled green alga, a protoctist whose 'body' consists of three regions. The base of *Acetabularia* contains the single nucleus. A short 'stem' leads to a hat-like structure, the shape of which varies from one species of *Acetabularia* to another. In *A. crenulata* the hat is spikey but in *A. mediterranea* the hat is shaped rather like an umbrella. These algae are truly gigantic in that their cells are about 30 mm long! They also have remarkable powers of recovery if they are damaged; if a hat is cut off, *Acetabularia* will obligingly grow another identical one!

So here we have a large single-celled organism with a hat, the shape of which depends upon the species. Since the nucleus is in the base of the alga, there must be some way in which the instructions in the DNA pass up through the stem to the hat. The two species of *Acetabularia* were used in an ingenious experiment. Each plant was cut into three pieces, base, stem and hat. The hats were discarded and the stems were swapped over so that the stem of *A. crenulata* was now attached to the base of *A. mediterranea* and vice-versa. After a short time, the plants recovered and developed new hats. The experiment, and the results are shown in Fig.1.18.

It is evident, from the results of this experiment, the type of hat which regenerates depends on information in the nucleus. It also shows that the information is able to pass through the stem of the alga and influence the way that the cytoplasm differentiates into a particular kind of hat. We now know that the information (i.e. the DNA-coded message) is copied into another molecule, messenger RNA (mRNA), and that this molecule conveys instructions to the cytoplasm of the cell. The mRNA can influence which proteins the cell can manufacture and thus determine how the cell will develop.

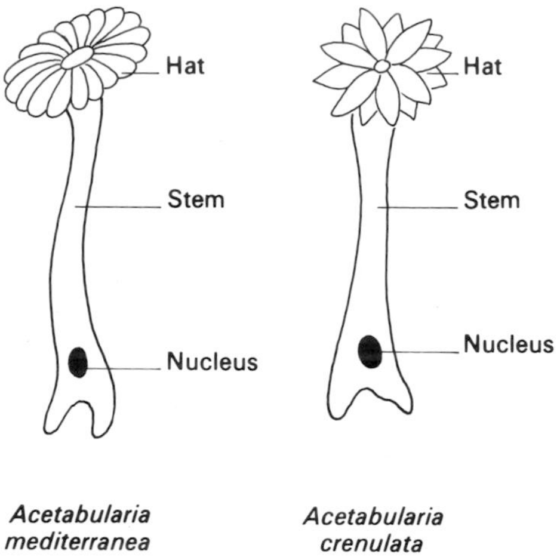
Hat
Stem
Nucleus
Hat
Stem
Nucleus
Acetabularia mediterranea
Acetabularia crenulata

Figure 1.17

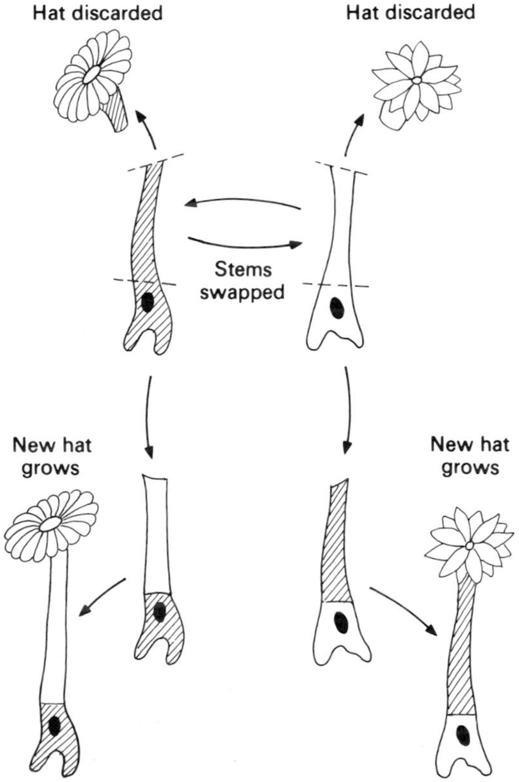
Hat discarded
Hat discarded
Stems swapped
New hat grows
New hat grows

Figure 1.18 Regeneration experiment

LIKE MAKES LIKE: THE DUPLICATION OF DNA

Watson and Crick were fortunate to be able to draw on a growing bank of information about DNA. In their article, published in *Nature* in April 1953, Watson and Crick revealed that their proposed structure for DNA was based largely on stereochemistry and acknowledged that more detailed X-ray work was still needed.

They knew that the ratios of the base pairs adenine to thymine (A:T) and guanine to cytosine (G:C) in DNA were both very close to 1:1 in all DNA examined. However, the ratios of adenine + thymine to guanine + cytosine differed from one species to another.

Watson and Crick attempted to make models. They tried to work in three dimensions. Eventually they hit on a structure which is now well known, i.e. the double helix. In a masterly piece of understatement they reported the following:

'It has not escaped our notice that the specific pairing we have postulated immediately suggests a possible copying mechanism for the genetic material.'

They had realised that the sequence of bases could form the basis of a chemical code and that to be able to pass this code to future generations of cells the molecule must have some way of making exact copies of itself. Subsequently they went on to say:

'Now our model for deoxyribonucleic acid is, in effect, a pair of templates each of which is complementary to the other. We imagine that prior to duplication the hydrogen bonds are broken, and the two chains unwind and separate. Each chain then acts as a template for the formation onto itself of a new companion chain, so that eventually we shall have two pairs of chains, where we only had one before. Moreover the sequence of pairs of bases will have been duplicated exactly.'

This means that the DNA molecule in a given cell is able to be copied exactly and then be passed on to the daughter cells. It is in this way that the genetically-coded instructions pass down through the generations. The mechanism of *semi-conservative* replication of DNA is shown in Fig.1.19.

Q Why do you think that DNA replication is described as semi-conservative?

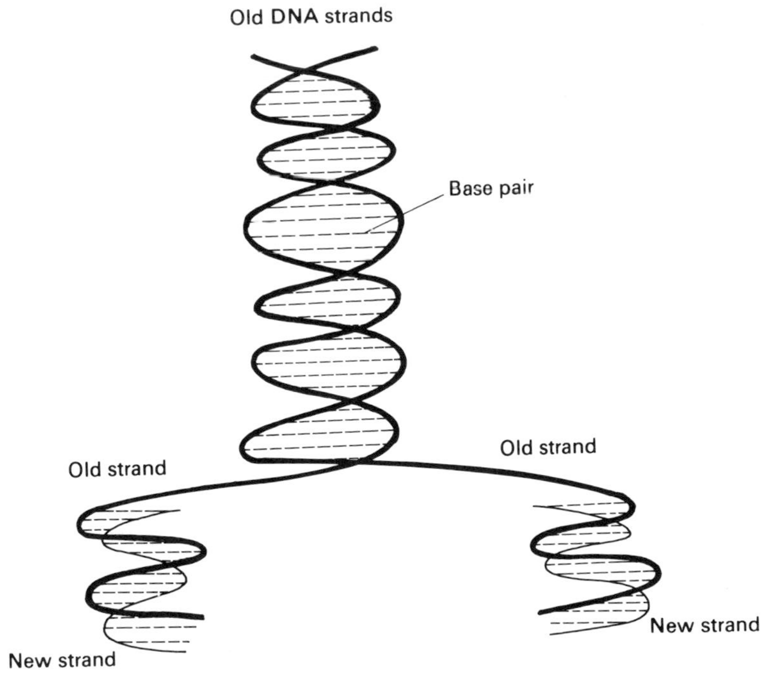
Old DNA strands
Base pair
Old strand
Old strand
New strand
New strand

Figure 1.19 Replication of DNA as proposed by Watson and Crick

Confirmation of the duplication of DNA

Watson and Crick showed the way forward for more research. It was now apparent that their hypothesis needed to be tested. This was done by M. Meselson and F. Stahl who, in 1958, used a heavy *isotope* of nitrogen ^{15}N to label replicating DNA.

The four bases used in the synthesis of DNA contain nitrogen. It is possible to synthesise these bases using the heavy isotope of nitrogen, ^{15}N, in place of the commonly-occurring light isotope of nitrogen, ^{14}N. DNA containing significant amounts of this heavy isotope is much denser than normal DNA and this difference can be detected by centrifugation (see Fig.1.20).

Meselson and Stahl grew the bacterium *Escherichia coli* on a nutrient medium containing heavy nitrogen. After many generations, the DNA extracted from the bacteria was found to be completely labelled with ^{15}N. This heavy DNA was readily detected and a dense band in the *centrifuged* extract.

They then transferred the bacteria to a nutrient medium containing light nitrogen and took samples at intervals which corresponded to the times at which the bacteria divided. These samples were then tested for the presence of labelled DNA using the technique of *density gradient centrifugation*. The first sample, taken after one division in the presence of the light nitrogen, revealed DNA of a density intermediate between the heavy ^{15}N-labelled DNA and the normal ^{14}N-labelled DNA. This suggested some kind of 'hybrid' DNA with equal amounts of ^{14}N and ^{15}N.

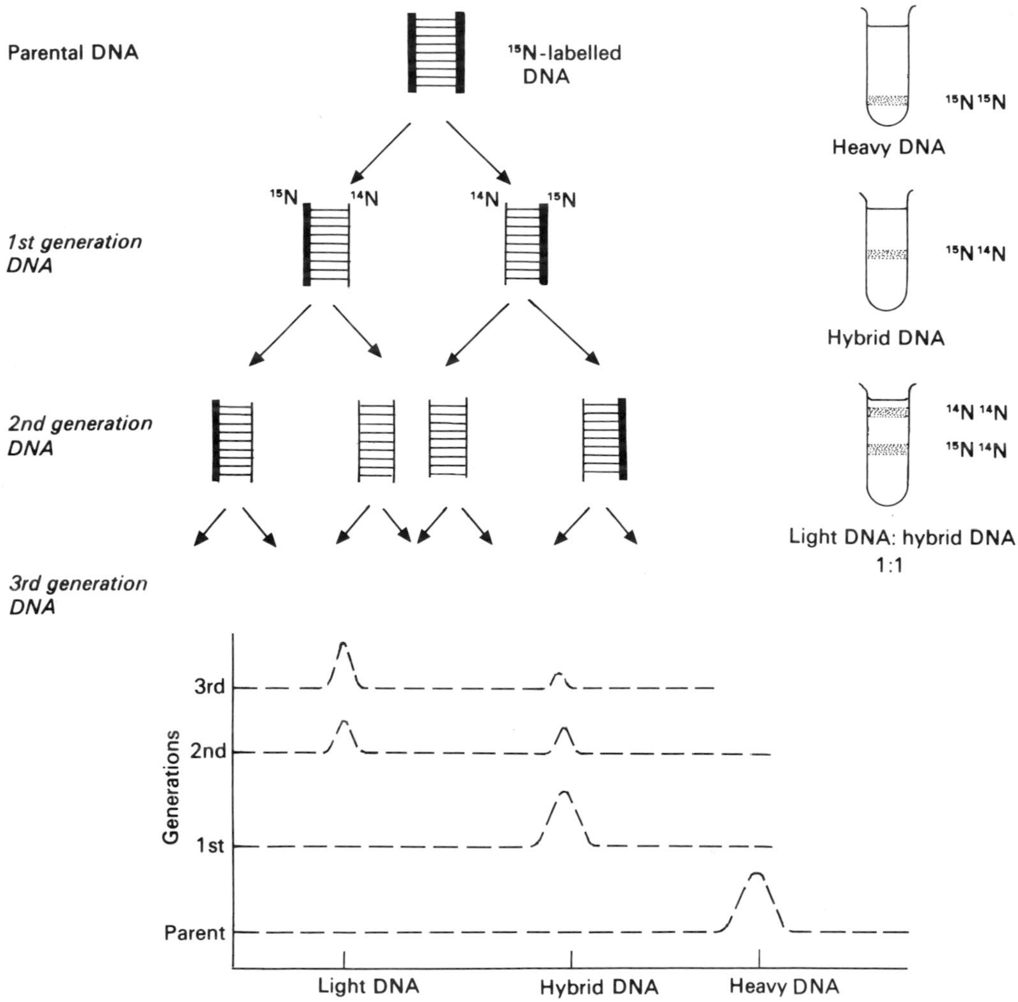
Parental DNA
15N-labelled DNA
15N 15N
Heavy DNA
15N
14N
14N
15N
1st generation DNA
15N 14N
Hybrid DNA
2nd generation DNA
14N 14N
15N 14N
Light DNA: hybrid DNA 1:1
3rd generation DNA
3rd
2nd
1st
Parent
Generations
Light DNA
Hybrid DNA
Heavy DNA

Figure 1.20 Meselson and Stahl's experiment

In the second sample, corresponding to two divisions in the presence of ^{14}N, two distinct bands of DNA were detected. One of the bands was of intermediate density, the other was similar to the normal ^{14}N DNA. This suggests that the DNA does indeed act as a template and so forms the basis of the model of *semi-conservative replication*.

Subsequent samples, taken after 3, 4, 5 generations, etc, lend even more weight to this interpretation.

Q Test your understanding of the above text by trying to predict the outcome of a third division and its effect on the relative amounts of DNA of different densities (see Fig 1.20). (See answer on page 98.)

DENSITY GRADIENT CENTRIFUGATION

A centrifuge is a device in which substances are separated by spinning them very rapidly. Molecules with slightly different densities are 'thrown down' by the exaggerated forces acting upon them. A density gradient consists of a tube containing 'layers' of different strengths of sucrose, the most dense being at the bottom of the tube and the most dilute being at the top. The substance to be separated is pipetted on to the top of the mixture and the tube is then spun in the centrifuge at very high speed. After a period of time, the more dense molecules will have settled further down the tube to form a distinct band. This technique is capable of separating 'heavy DNA' from 'light DNA' and can also show 'intermediate DNA' which has both ^{14}N and ^{15}N atoms in the base molecules.

ISOTOPES

Isotopes are alternative forms of the same atom. Some isotopes have an extra particle, called a neutron, in their atomic nucleus. Heavy isotopes contain these extra neutrons and can be used to label certain substances in the cell. By detecting where the heavy isotopes are used in the cell, it is possible to discover where and in which order these chemical reactions take place.

LIKE FATHER, LIKE SON

It may be hard to believe, but in your distant past you were once a tiny single cell created by the fusion of two special cells called gametes. One of the gametes, the sperm, came from your father. The other gamete, the ovum, came from your mother. The fusion of these gametes took place in your mother's oviduct and the process called fertilisation took place and marked the creation of a unique person - you! Over the next nine months the newly made single-celled zygote went through a lot of changes which are collectively defined as development.

In the early stages of development the single cell divides continually to produce a multicellular ball of cells called an embryo. Cell division continues but the cells start to show definite signs of being different - they are said to have become specialised to fulfil specific functions. Also obvious is the change in shape in the development from an embryo to a fetus. A fetus is clearly not a mass of *identical* cells despite the fact that it began life as a single cell.

Within days of the great event of your birth relatives and friends may comment on how "you've got your mother's nose" or "you've got your father's eyes". You may even look like a grandparent. These likenesses become more apparent as you get older.

All these observations raise a number of questions. How does a single fertilised cell make the six million million or so cells that you are now made of? How do these cells specialise? What do sperm and egg cells contain which could make us look similar to our parents? We will try to answer these questions in the following chapters.

MULTIPLE CHOICE QUESTIONS

1. 20% of the bases in a DNA molecule are guanine. What percentage of the bases are thymine?

A 20%
B 30%
C 60%
D 80%

2. Translation is the

A copying of a sequence of DNA nucleotides to form a complementary DNA strand.
B reading of a mRNA molecule to produce a polypeptide chain.
C copying of a DNA nucleotide sequence to produce a molecule of mRNA.
D reading of a DNA molecule to produce a polypeptide chain.

3. The five bases found in nucleic acids are adenine (A), cytosine (C), guanine (G), thymine (T) and uracil (U).
In individuals with normal haemoglobin, the mRNA includes the codon GAA. This sequence is altered in individuals with sickle cell anaemia so that their mRNA has an alternative codon GUA at the same location.
This suggests that the DNA has undergone a mutation involving a change of base sequence from

A CAA to TAA.
B CTT to CAT.
C GTT to GAT.
D CTT to CTA.

4. Radioactive tracers can be used to locate sites of chemical synthesis in a cell. Which one of the following can be used to pinpoint the site of mRNA synthesis in the nucleus?

A ^{3}H in uracil.
B ^{3}H in thymine.
C ^{32}P in phosphate.
D ^{14}C in ribulose.

5. Protein synthesis involves several steps that are listed below.

1 The translation of mRNA by a ribosome.
2 The joining of amino acids to form a polypeptide.
3 The transcription of DNA to form a mRNA molecule.
4 Movement of mRNA from the nucleus to the cytoplasm.

Which of the following sequences correctly describes the process of protein synthesis?

A 1 3 2 4.
B 3 4 2 1.
C 1 2 4 3.
D 3 4 1 2.

6. A molecule of DNA is allowed to replicate in the presence of ^{3}H labelled thymine. Which of the following statements about the newly replicated DNA molecule is true?

A Both strands are made of newly synthesised nucleotides.
B One strand will be radioactive and the other strand will be unradioactive.
C Both strands will contain approximately equal amounts of ^{3}H labelled thymine.
D All the newly assembled nucleotides will contain ^{3}H labelled bases.

(See answers on page 98.)

CHAPTER 2

TWO TYPES OF CELL DIVISION

INTRODUCTION

In the young human animal, the rate of cell production exceeds the rate of cell death and so growth occurs. The adult body, however, usually maintains a constant mass and so the two rates are regulated in a steady state. Nevertheless, not all cell types grow and reproduce at the same rate. For example, intestinal cells and some white blood cells have an average life of only a few days whilst red blood cells have an average life of 100 days, and in a healthy liver, cells seldom die. It is also of interest to note that there is little or no replacement of brain cells – only a gradual loss with ageing!

Normally, a carefully regulated system determines how the cells grow and divide but sometimes the mechanism breaks down so that a *clone* of cells derived from one cell can develop and form a *tumour* of unwanted cells. This happens more frequently in older organisms and the tumour is usually restricted to its area of origin; it is said to be *benign* and causes little harm to the individual (e.g. a wart). Tumours become a significant medical problem only when they spread from the area of origin to other parts of the body (i.e. they become *malignant* and cause cancer).

It is quite difficult to study cells in a living organism (i.e. *in vivo*). For this reason test tube (i.e. *in vitro*) techniques have been developed to grow cells in culture at 37°C in a nutrient medium usually containing 5-20% blood serum. Under sterile conditions, human fetal cells can be maintained for about 50 divisions (so a small sample of 10^6 cells will produce more than 10^{21} cells – equivalent to the mass of about 10^8 people!).

Some cells in culture undergo a change which establishes a strain of immortal cells or cell line. One cell line of human tumour cells, the HeLa strain, has been cultured and studied for many years and has provided a great deal of information on cell biology and the cell cycle of growth and division.

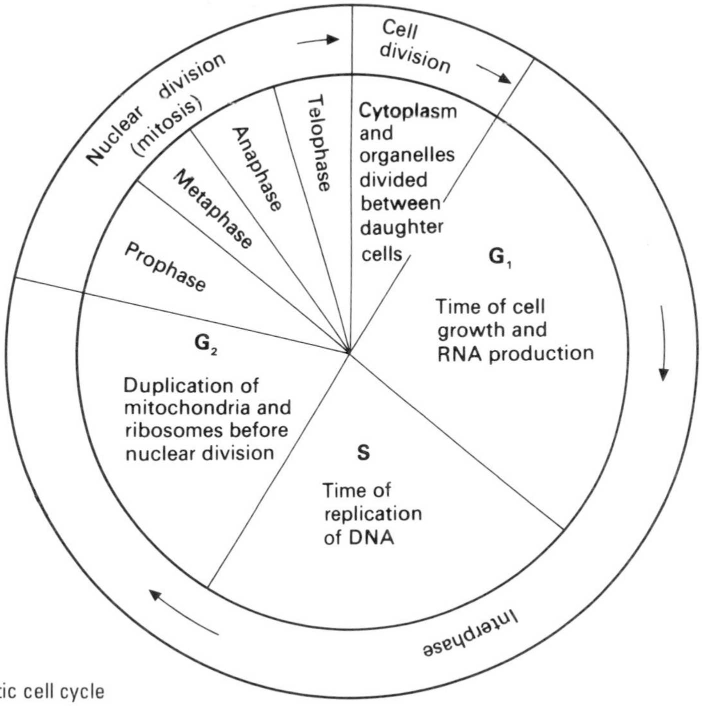

Cell division
Nuclear division (mitosis)
Telophase
Anaphase
Metaphase
Prophase
Cytoplasm and organelles divided between daughter cells
G₁
Time of cell growth and RNA production
G₂
Duplication of mitochondria and ribosomes before nuclear division
S
Time of replication of DNA
Interphase

Figure 2.1 Generalised eukaryotic cell cycle

MITOSIS - 'THE DIVISION OF BODY CELLS'

The process by which a single-celled zygote becomes a ball of cells is called *mitosis*. It is a type of cell division, a term which is sometimes confusing because in reality the process involves cells multiplying in number. The first mitotic cell division of the zygote produces two cells which are identical in the respect that they have exactly the same number and type of chromosomes (see Fig.2.2).

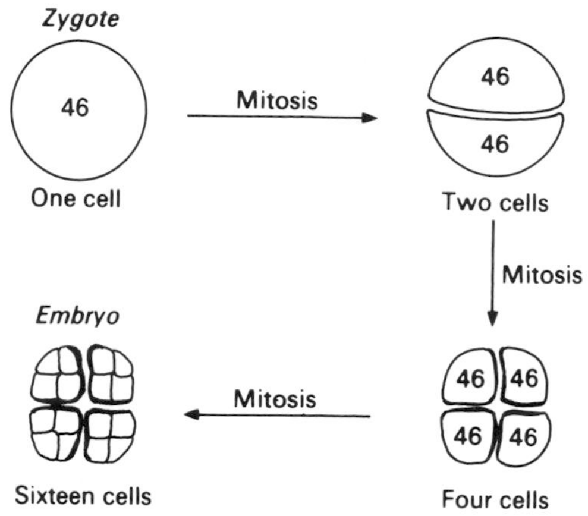
Zygote
46
One cell
Mitosis
46
46
Two cells
Mitosis
Embryo
Mitosis
46
46
46
46
Sixteen cells
Four cells

Figure 2.2 In the ball of cells produced by mitotic cell division of the human zygote, each cell contains 46 chromosomes

In humans, each body (or somatic) cell nucleus contains 46 chromosomes. The total number of chromosomes in a body cell nucleus is called the diploid number. The *diploid number* for humans is therefore 46, but other organisms have a different diploid number (see Table 2.1).

Species	Chromosome number
Algerian gerbil	40
Cabbage	18
Chicken	36
Crocus	6
Fruit fly	8
House mouse	40
Kangaroo	12
Lycaenid butterfly	446
Man	46
Nematode worm	2
Potato	48
Sweet pea	14
Wheat	42

Table 2.1 Chromosome numbers show great variation between species. Note that all are even numbers as the diploid chromosomes occur in pairs

The nucleus of the human zygote also has the diploid number of 46 chromosomes. The first mitotic cell division of the zygote produces two cells each with 46 chromosomes. These cells then divide to produce four cells each with 46 chromosomes and so the process continues. How does mitotic cell division ensure that the cells produced always have the same number of chromosomes? Fortunately, scientists have been able to find out the answer to this question by using stains which show up the chromosomes during mitosis (see Fig.2.3).

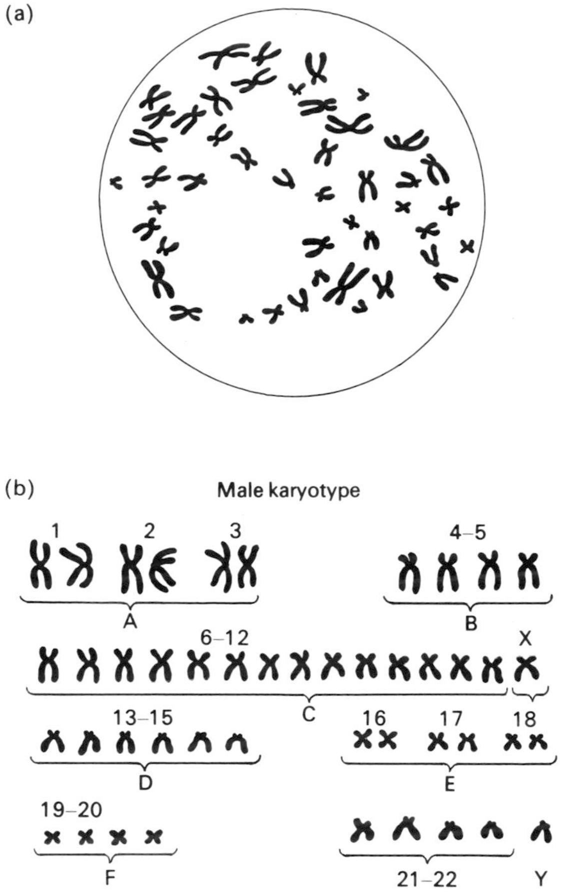
(a)
(b)
Male karyotype
1
2
3
4–5
A
B
6–12
X
C
13–15
16
17
18
D
E
19–20
F
21–22
Y

Figure 2.3 (a) Chromosomes from a man's body cell which was undergoing division are treated with a salt solution and stained. (b) The chromosomes are then grouped in pairs to produce a karyotype. There are 22 pairs of autosomes and 1 pair of sex chromosomes (in this case, an X and a Y)

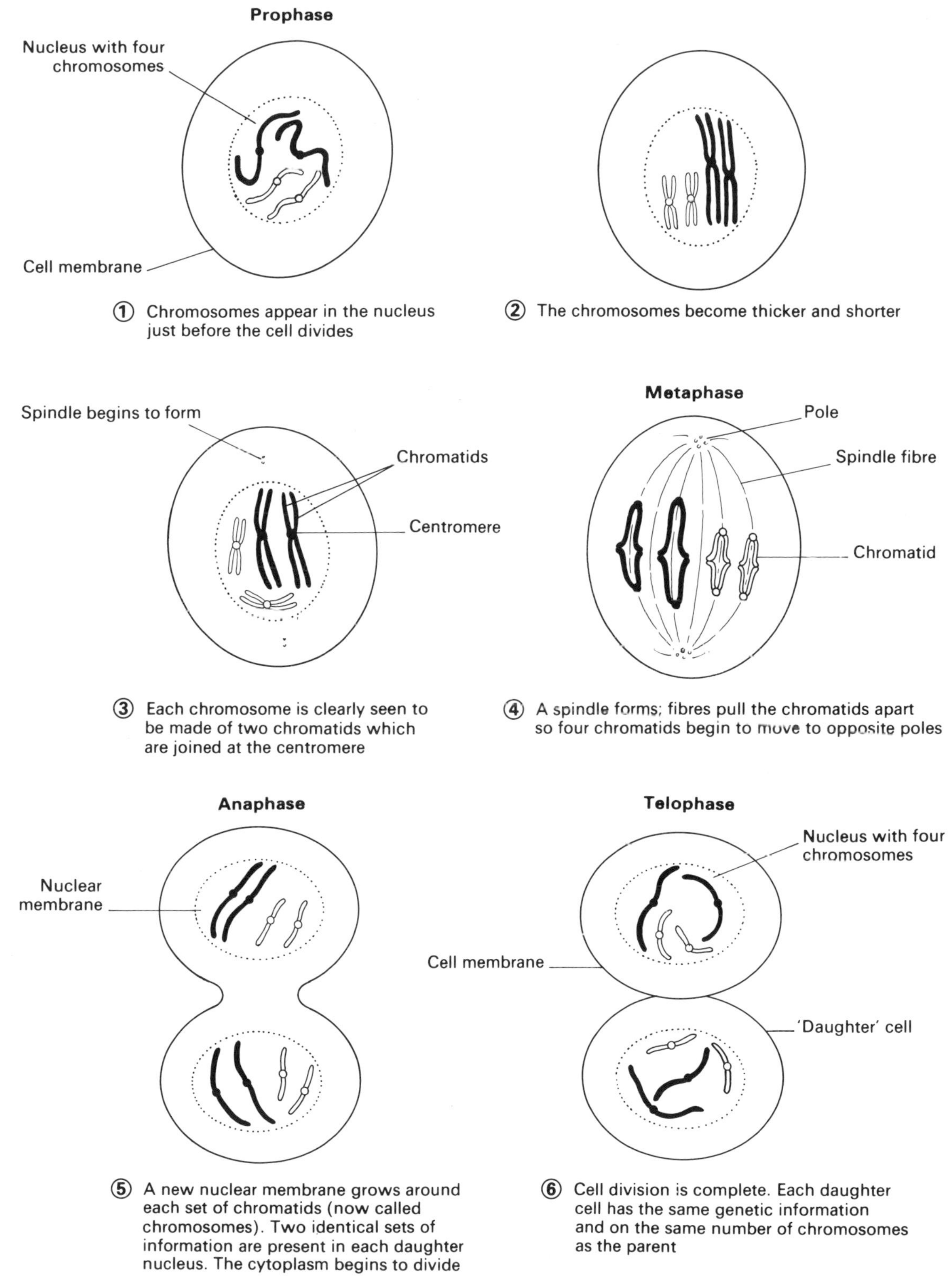
Prophase
Nucleus with four chromosomes
Cell membrane
① Chromosomes appear in the nucleus just before the cell divides
② The chromosomes become thicker and shorter
Spindle begins to form
Chromatids
Centromere
Metaphase
Pole
Spindle fibre
Chromatid
③ Each chromosome is clearly seen to be made of two chromatids which are joined at the centromere
④ A spindle forms; fibres pull the chromatids apart so four chromatids begin to move to opposite poles
Anaphase
Nuclear membrane
Telophase
Nucleus with four chromosomes
Cell membrane
'Daughter' cell
⑤ A new nuclear membrane grows around each set of chromatids (now called chromosomes). Two identical sets of information are present in each daughter nucleus. The cytoplasm begins to divide
⑥ Cell division is complete. Each daughter cell has the same genetic information and on the same number of chromosomes as the parent

Figure 2.4 Mitosis. The division of body cells. The process is a continuous one but biologists artificially split it into several distinct stages

At first, the chromosomes look jumbled up in a way that makes them look all tangled together. They then get shorter and thicker in a stage called the *prophase*. Before this happens, each chromosome will have made an *identical* copy of itself called a chromatid. In fact, each chromosome is made up of its two chromatids which are held together at a place called the *centromere*. During prophase the nuclear membrane in the cell disappears.

The next stage is called *metaphase*. During this stage the chromosomes are clearly seen to be separate from each other. In the diagram they have been drawn queueing up in single file in the middle of the cell (this is not strictly accurate but it helps understanding!). Each centromere is attached by fibres running to the two 'poles'. The chromatids of each chromosome are pulled apart from each other in the next stage, called *anaphase*. It seems as though the fibres attached to the poles begin to shorten to help this to happen.

Each side of the cell now has exactly the same number of chromatids. At this point the chromatids are called chromosomes again. You will recall that earlier it was stated that a chromatid is an identical copy of a chromosome, so the name change is understandable, even if it is a little confusing. The last stage is called *Telophase*. Nuclear membranes now form around each set of the 'new' chromosomes and a new cell membrane forms to separate them into two cells. Examples of these events can be seen in Fig.2.4 where for simplicity, the original cell only contains four chromosomes – 46 is too many to include.

In mitotic cell division each new cell is called a *daughter cell*. The cell which gives rise to the daughter cells is called a *parent cell*. The main point to remember about mitosis is that the daughter cells contain exactly the same number and type of chromosomes as the original parent cell. The daughter cells are thus identical to each other because each of the original chromosomes is replicated *before* mitosis.

Mitosis is a very important process in living organisms. It is the cell division of growth and it is used to replace worn out cells. It is the method used by some organisms to reproduce asexually and it is also the type of cell division used by a cancerous tumour.

■ LOOKING FOR STAGES OF MITOSIS

It is possible to see the stages of mitosis in the cells of some plant root tips. (Germinating broad bean seeds or onion bulbs held over water produce suitable root tip material.) The last 5mm of root tip must be cut off and placed in dilute hydrochloric acid which has been prewarmed to 60°C in a water bath. The tip must be left in the acid for about 6 to 7 minutes. It is then washed in water and placed on a microscope slide. A drop of methylene blue stain is then added and left on the root tip for about 3 minutes. A coverslip can then be gently pressed against the tip to squash it. Gentle rotation of the squashed cells using a finger helps to make the cells easier to see under the microscope. If you look carefully you should be able to see stained chromosomes at various stages of mitosis. The best place to look is near the very end of the tip. In the other parts of the root tip the cells are elongated and specialising.

Figure 2.5

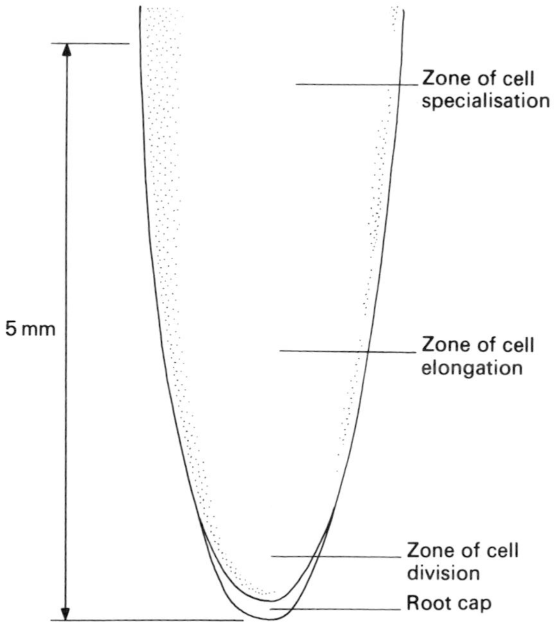
5 mm
Zone of cell specialisation
Zone of cell elongation
Zone of cell division
Root cap

■ THE SAME YET DIFFERENT!

The fact that DNA is capable of replicating (making exact copies of itself) has great significance. Bound up in the sequence of bases are the unique sets of instructions which make you different from anything or anyone else on Earth (unless you are an identical twin!). When cells divide, they first copy their DNA and then they pass one copy to each of the daughter cells. Since we all started life as a single cell, all of the cells in our body might be expected to contain the same copies of DNA. Some cells are exceptions, for instance mature red blood cells lack a nucleus and so do not follow this generalisation, and gametes contain only half as much DNA as normal body cells.

The understanding that DNA is a self-replicating molecule capable of passing instructions from cell to cell raises an important issue. Since cells have the same sets of instructions, you might expect them all to be the same but this is clearly not the case. Shortly after you were conceived, the fertilised egg began to divide. Within a few days you were a ball of cells and within a few weeks, you were a recognisable fetus with cells of different types. Just as you are today, a complex organism of different types of cells, so you were then. A simple analogy would be to consider a class of schoolchildren each one reading from the same textbook but with each child reading from a different page. Each child is reading different information but all of the children have access to the same information if they so wished. In the same sort of way, each of your cells is capable of 'reading' only the set of instructions which applies to them. Somehow, potential kidney cells 'know' that they are different and begin to specialise by reading only the information that they need. This process is termed *differentiation*.

There are several hypotheses which help to explain differentiation. Perhaps cells only retain what information they need or perhaps they switch off the parts of the messages which they do not need. An indication of what might be happening comes from a study of frog embryos.

■ The totipotency theory

When an embryo begins to grow, it also begins to *differentiate*. In the early stages of development, all the cells in the embryo look more or less similar. After a while, definite structures form and clearly the cells become different from each other (i.e. specialised). Even before the obvious signs of specialisation are visible, however, it is possible to construct fate maps which predict what structures cells eventually become. The accuracy of these fate maps become greater as the embryo gets older. In the early stages it seems that cells have the ability to become almost any structure. The ability of one cell to develop into any type of cell is called *totipotency*.

The totipotency idea was first tested by transplanting nuclei from various tissues into newly fertilised frog's eggs (see Fig 2.6).

Freshly fertilised frog's eggs are irradiated so that their own nuclei are destroyed. Using microsurgery, nuclei are removed from cells of various ages and degrees of specialisation and inserted into the irradiated eggs. This produces a new egg with a donor nucleus which is then left to develop. The survival rate of these 'donor-host' embryo experiments are summarised in Table 2.2.

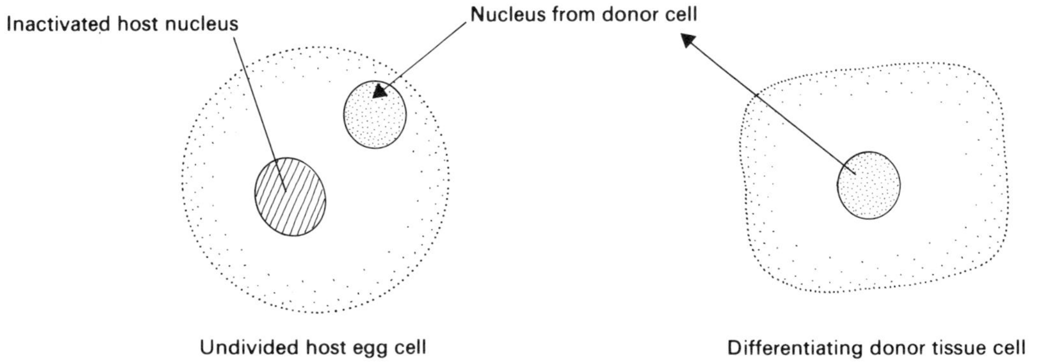
Inactivated host nucleus
Nucleus from donor cell
Undivided host egg cell
Differentiating donor tissue cell

Figure 2.6 Transplanting a nucleus from a differentiated cell from a donor embryo into an irradiated fertilised egg (i.e. the host nucleus has been destroyed)

Age of donor embryo (in hours) from which the nucleus is removed	Percentage of 'donor-host' embryos surviving at different stages (in hours after fertilisation) of development				
	10	12	25-30	Swimming tadpole stage 120	Feeding tadpole stage
6	100	98	94	85	81
12	100	100	98	79	77
25-30	100	96	79	53	52
Hatching 58	100	76	59	36	27
Swimming 120	100	80	54	19	15

Table 2.2 Survival rates of different 'donor-host' frog embryos

If specialisation is a result of cells 'switching off' their DNA signals, we might expect a low survival rate if the donor nuclei are chosen from older, more specialised types of cells. On the other hand, if after specialisation cells only retain the parts of DNA which they require, no subsequent development of 'donor-host' embryos would be expected since vital information would be absent in the donor nuclei.

Q 1. Do you think that the results summarised in Table 2.2 support the theory of totipotency?

2. What do you think would be likely to happen if the 'switching off' hypothesis was incorrect?

3. Use the results in the table to plot a graph of the percentage success against the development stage finally reached by the embryos. Does the data and the graph support the switching off hypothesis? (See answer on page 98.)

Plant tissue culture

Evidence of genes being activated by chemical substances comes from experiments on plant tissue culture. Small fragments of carrot can be grown on sterile nutrients producing a bunch of undifferentiated cells known as a *callus*. By adding plant hormones, it is possible to persuade this tissue to differentiate into roots, shoots or leaves. A whole plant can be produced from a single cell indicating that plants are quite capable of regenerating themselves. Indeed plants seem to be quite adept at replacing lost and damaged tissue showing that the DNA messages are present but are repressed by chemicals in their vicinity .

The Jacob-Monod concept of the gene

In 1960 Francois Jacob and Jacques Monod proposed that genes were sections of DNA which could be switched on or off by certain molecules. Genes appear to be controlled by the interaction of protein molecules (i.e. *repressors*) with certain specific sites on the DNA. These repressor molecules prevent the transcription of the gene so that the synthesis of mRNA is blocked. As a result of Jacob and Monod's work, it is now widely accepted that genes can be, and are, switched on and off.

A series of complex experiments using bacteriophage viruses performed by Walter Gilbert, Benno Muller-Hill and Mark Ptashne in America, demonstrated the existence of these repressor molecules and the mechanisms involved in gene regulation.

MUM, DAD, MEIOSIS AND ME

You now know that you began life as a zygote and that the processes of mitosis and cell specialisation helped to continue your development. A zygote is formed by the fertilisation (or fusion) of the male and female gametes. These special sex cells are different from the somatic (or general body) cells in one very important way – they contain half the number of chromosomes. So, since all human body cells contain the diploid number of 46 chromosomes, a sperm or egg cell will contain half this number, that is, 23. This number is called the haploid number.

Q Examine the data in Table 2.3. What evidence is there to support the information given in the above paragraph?

The parts of your body which make the sex cells are called *gonads*. In a male, the gonads are the *testes*. In a female, they are the *ovaries*. Whatever helps you to look similar to your parents must be found inside the gamete cells which fused to produce your zygote. Your earlier reading ought to help you appreciate that it is the DNA contained in the gametes which is the all important ingredient.

There are diploid cells inside the gonads which undergo a type of cell division which produces the haploid gametes. This type of cell division is called *meiosis*. If you can understand what happens to the chromosomes of a cell during meiosis you will find understanding genetics much easier. So, what does happen?

Before answering this question it is important that you appreciate that in body cells the chromosomes occur in definite pairs. Scientists have been able to show this by staining the chromosomes to make them visible and then taking photographs which can be magnified. In this way the chromosomes can be looked at very easily and scientists find that they can be arranged into pairs based on their size and the position of the centromere. The process is called *karyotyping*.

Because each pair of chromosomes seems to be alike they are said to be *homologous* to each other. Each homologous pair of chromosomes is given a number to distinguish it from a different homologous pair. For 22 pairs of homologous chromosomes the two chromosomes of the pair always look similar. These chromosomes are called *autosomes* and they are made up of the genes for most of your characteristics. There is one final pair of the homologous chromosomes in which the two chromosomes of the pair do not always look alike. These chromosomes are not given a number, instead they are given the letters **X** and **Y**. If you have a pair of these chromosomes made up of two **X**s (i.e. **XX**), you will be female. If you have a pair of chromosomes made up of an **X** and a **Y** (i.e. **XY**), you will be a male. The **X** and **Y** chromosomes are called the *sex chromosomes* and they carry genes which are responsible for sexual characteristics.

Meiosis is the process by which the somatic cells (diploid) of the gonads give rise to the gametic cells (haploid). Meiosis is best thought of as two stages of cell division. The first stage separates each member of a homologous pair of chromosomes, and the second stage separates the chromatids of which each chromosome is made.

Species	DNA/mg x 10^{-5}			
	Nucleus of erythrocyte	Nucleus of liver cell	Sperm	Sperm (x2)
Domestic fowl	2.34	2.39	1.26	2.52
Shark	1.97	2.01	0.91	1.82
Carp	3.49	3.33	1.64	3.28
Brown trout	5.79		2.67	5.34
Toad	7.33		3.70	7.40

Table 2.3 The DNA content of different somatic and gametic cells

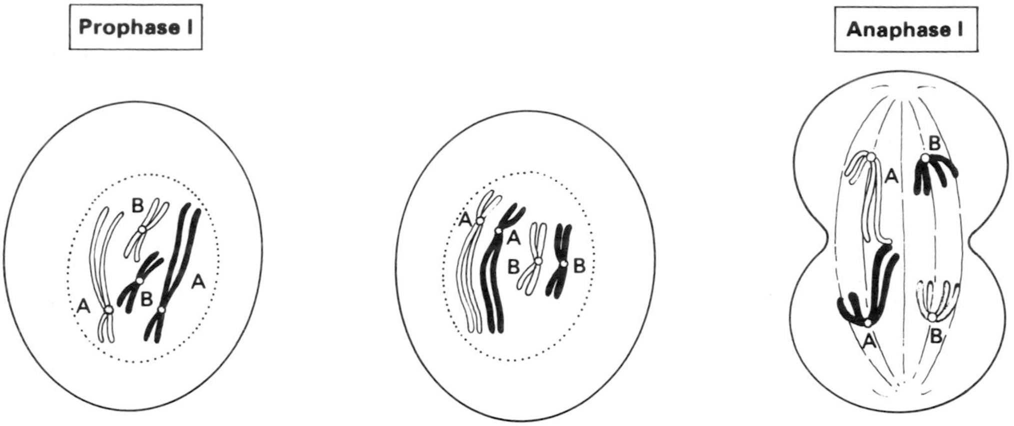
Prophase I
Anaphase I
A
B
A
B
A
B
A
B
B
A
B
A
B
A

1. The chromosomes shorten. The light-coloured ones are from the mother, the dark-coloured ones are from the father (i.e. $2n = 4$). Each chromosome consists of two strands called chromatids, joined at the centre or centromere

2. Homologous chromosomes lie alongside each other. They are termed bivalents

3. The nuclear membrane breaks down, the spindle appears and whole chromosomes move to opposite poles, thus reducing the number of chromosomes at each pole by half

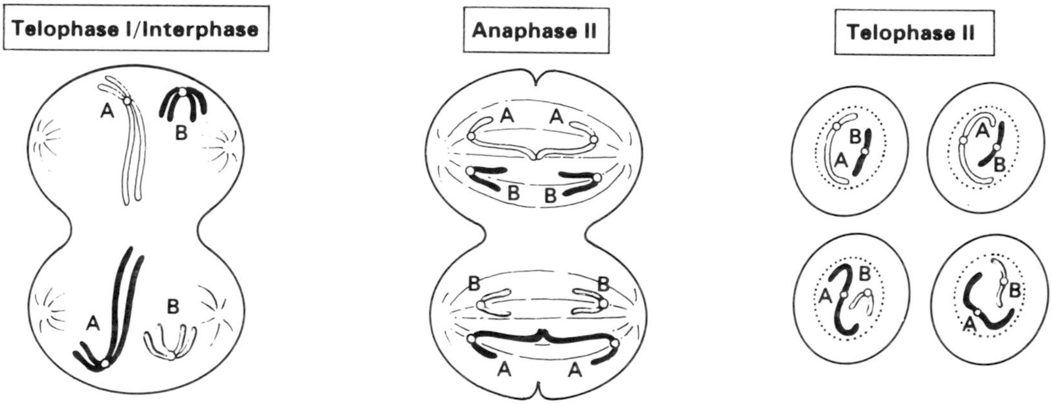
Telophase I/Interphase
Anaphase II
Telophase II
A
B
A
B
A
A
B
B
B
B
A
A
B
A
A
B
B
A
A
B

4. Two sets of haploid nuclei are formed. Each chromosome is clearly made up of two chromatids.

5. Two spindles form at right angles to the original one. The chromatids are pulled to opposite poles

6. After telophase II and cell division there are four haploid nuclei (i.e. $n = 2$)

Figure 2.7 Meiosis. Note that, for simplicity, only four chromosomes are shown in the initial somatic diploid cell

The first stage involves the duplication of the chromosomal DNA at interphase in much the same way as happens in mitosis. So, each chromosome is now made of two chromatids joined by the centromere.

In the next phase the chromosomes shorten and thicken, spindle fibres appear (and also centrioles in animals), and the nuclear membrane disappears. So far it sounds just like mitosis, but the following phase represents the major differences between the two types of cell division. In mitosis the chromosomes are scattered individually in the cell but in meiosis they match up with each other in their homologous pairs (or *bivalents*). When the fibres pull on the centromeres the homologous chromosomes are pulled to opposite ends of the cell. The cell then divides into two as in mitosis. These two new cells only contain half the number of chromosomes (i.e. they are now haploids).

The final stage of meiosis separates the chromatids of each of the chromosomes in the two new cells. In this stage the chromatids behave in much the same way as they do in mitosis. The end result is four cells, each containing the haploid number of chromatids (now called chromosomes). The events of meiosis are shown in Fig.2.7.

	MITOSIS	MEIOSIS
Function	Production of somatic cells	Production of gametes
End products	Two daughter cells each with the diploid (2*n*) number of chromosomes	Four daughter cells each with the haploid (*n*) number of chromosomes
Number of divisions	One chromosome replication One cell division	One chromosome replication Two cell divisions
Behaviour of chromosomes	Each chromosome behaves entirely independently	Pairing takes place between homologous chromosomes
DNA replication	In S period of interphase before cell enters into division. Each chromosome replicates into two sister chromatids	In interphase before first division. Each chromosome replicates into two sister chromatids
Time of separation of sister chromatids	Anaphase Sister chromatids separate at the centrometre and move to the opposite poles of the spindle	Anaphase of second meiotic division. Sister chromatids remain attached at the centromere throughout the first meiotic division
Consequences	Daughter cells have identical chromosome number to parent cell. Daughter cells are genetically identical to parent cells. There has been no exchange of genetic material between homologous chromosomes	Daughter cells have half the chromosome number of parent cell. Independent assortment of chromosomes and crossing over in the chiasma of prophase I means new genotypes are produced (see page 28). The products of meiosis are genetically different. Meiosis generates genetic variability.

Table 2.4 Comparing and contrasting mitosis and meiosis

VARIETY IS THE SPICE OF LIFE

A link can be established between the behaviour of chromosomes and the pattern of the inheritance of Mendel's factors - the alleles of observable characteristics. During mitosis each daughter cell receives an identical copy of the DNA. In the process of meiosis, however, the pairs of chromosomes are split so that the chromosomes of paternal and maternal origin are divided between the gametes. There is no rule to say that the original sets must remain together. In fact, an independent assortment ensures a random mixture of the parents' chromosomes (and DNA). This gives rise to an increased variation in the offspring.

Variety is also increased by the formation of chiasmata due to crossing over (see page 68). When in meiosis, homologous chromosomes pair, parts of their chromatids can be exchanged - so the new chromatids can be found in gametes with different linkage of genes.

ALL ABOUT 'EVE'

At fertilisation a male nucleus enters a female cell and the zygote formed will consist of the diploid nucleus surrounded by the original female cell cytoplasm. This will, of course, have mitochondria containing mitochondrial DNA (mtDNA). This means that all of us - male and female - have the mtDNA inherited from our mothers and their mothers and so on. . .! This has happened, with small changes, going back at least half a million years to the original 'Eve' - which we probably must interpret as a population of at least 5000 breeding females. Analysis of mtDNA is helping to establish questions of human evolution and ethnic relationships.

■ MULTIPLE CHOICE QUESTIONS

1. The graph below shows the level of DNA in a cell which is undergoing cell division. Which of the following statements correctly describes the source of this data?

A Cell division leading to the formation of a pollen grain.
B Cell division leading to the formation of an ovum.
C Cell division leading to the formation of a skin cell.
D Cell division leading to the formation of sperm cells.

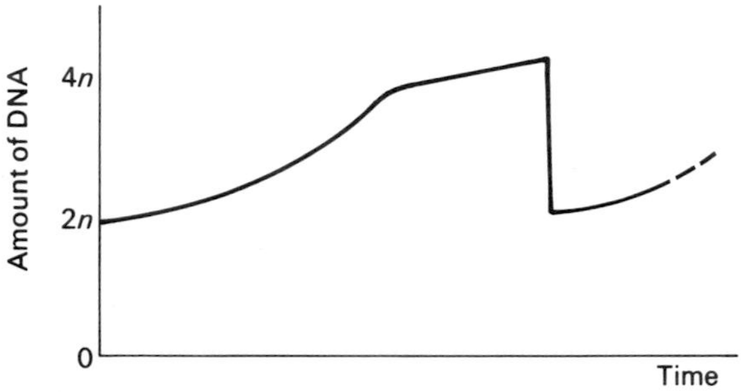

Amount of DNA
4n
2n
0
Time

2. The diagrams below show five stages in the process of mitotic cell division. Which sequence correctly describes the order of these stages in mitosis?

A 3 4 1 2 5.
B 2 3 4 1 5.
C 3 2 4 1 5.
D 3 1 5 2 4.

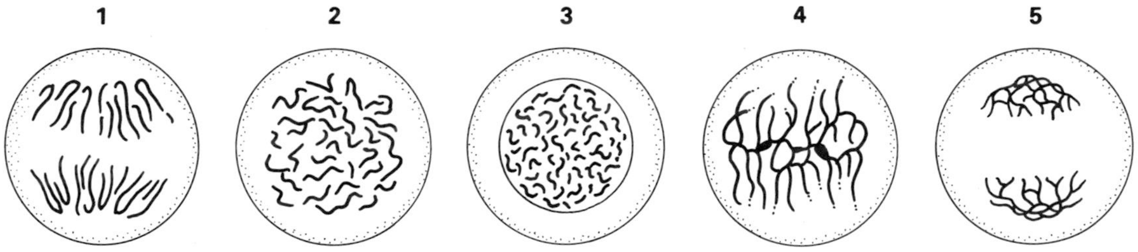

1
2
3
4
5

3. The diagram below shows a sperm mother cell of *Drosophila*. The chromosomes derived from each parent are shaded differently.

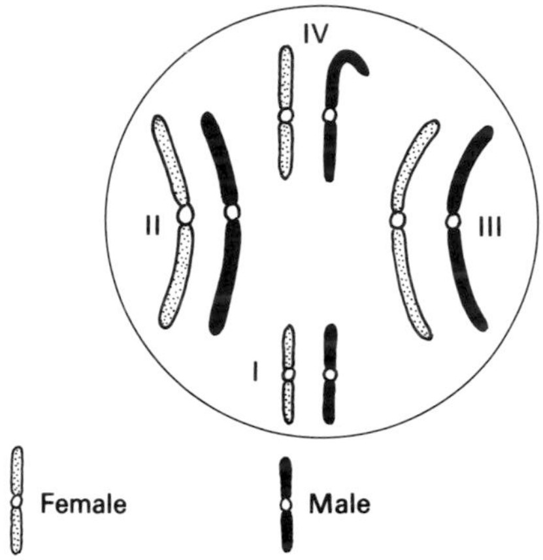

IV
II
III
I
Female
Male

What is the probability of a sperm receiving all four paternal chromosomes?

A 1 in 16.
B 1 in 8.
C 1 in 4.
D 1 in 2.
E Nil

(See answers on page 98.)

CHAPTER 3

MEIOSIS AND INHERITANCE

INTRODUCTION

Consider a genetic disease where the sufferer has to be 'pounded' regularly by a physiotherapist to loosen the abnormal amount of mucus in the lungs and allow normal breathing .... or another which damages red corpuscles, yet gives some protection from malaria .... and a third where in middle age the sufferer becomes clumsy, has slurred speech, a gradual deterioration in mental and physical abilities and which leads to an early death. Three sad conditions, yet some progress is being made in understanding the problems of each.

In the first example, cystic fibrosis, after much painstaking research the gene is now known in terms of its exact structure and its position on the chromosome. Understanding the second disease, sickle cell anaemia (see page 10), has stimulated study into DNA triplet coding sequences and it is now known that a single base change in the DNA can lead to an early death from acute anaemia, and heart and kidney failure. Yet a person who is a heterozygote (see page 32) suffers only mild anaemia. This person also has an advantage over others if living in a malaria region in that the malaria parasite is less able to survive in the presence of the abnormal sickle cell haemoglobin. In the third example, Huntington's chorea, a test has been developed to establish whether other members of the family carry the fatal gene.

In this chapter, we will look at some case studies and pose important ethical questions; but first we will consider meiosis as the basis of inheritance.

MEIOSIS AND INHERITANCE

Because meiosis is the process by which gametes are made, it plays an important part in genetics. After all, genetics is the study of inherited characteristics, and these characteristics are determined by genes found on the chromosomes which are present in the eggs and sperms produced by the parents.

To explain the link between meiosis and inheritance it is best to look at a specific example of *monohybrid inheritance*, i.e. the inheritance of *one* characteristic. Most people have a certain amount of skin pigmentation. This is because they possess the DNA which codes for the enzymes that are used to make melanin in skin cells (see page 4). However, there are some people who cannot make melanin because they lack one enzyme which converts tyrosine into dihydroxyphenylalanine (an intermediate compound). As a result, people who cannot make this enzyme lack skin pigmentation - they are said to be albino. Albinism can also occur in animals.

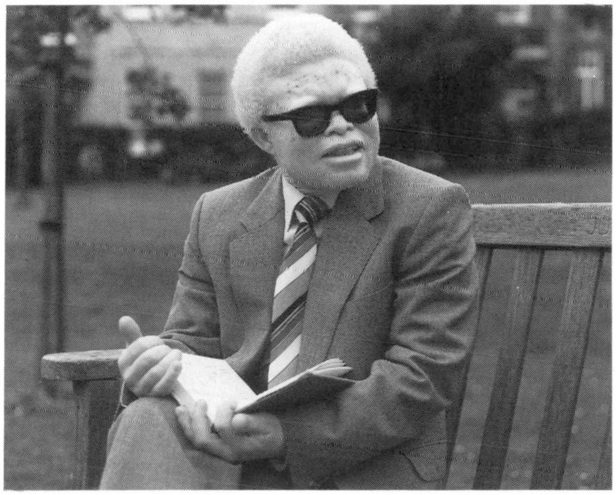

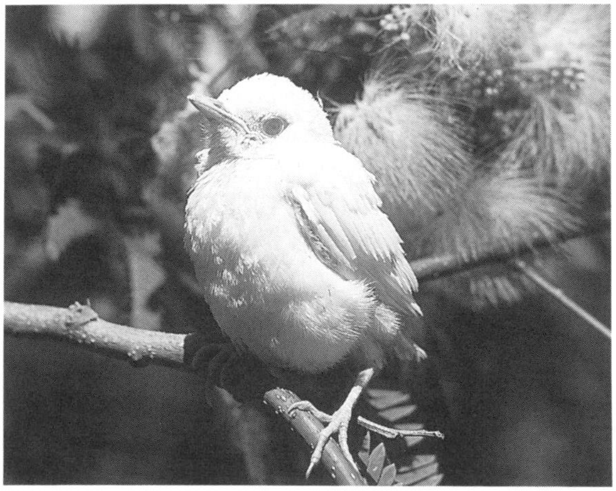

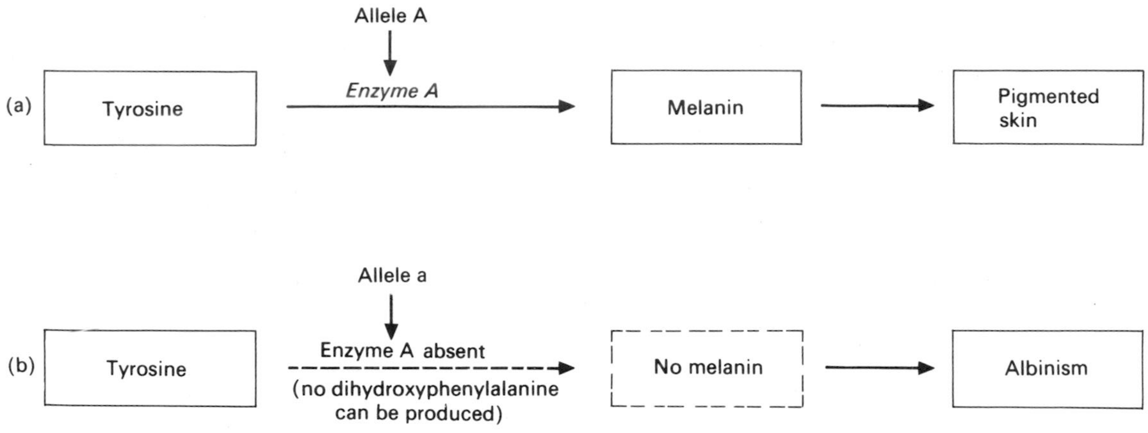
Allele A
Enzyme A
(a) Tyrosine
Melanin
Pigmented skin
Allele a
Enzyme A absent
(b) Tyrosine
(no dihydroxyphenylalanine can be produced)
No melanin
Albinism

Figure 3.1 The biochemistry of albinism

In these particular albinos a piece of DNA is altered in a way which prevents it from making the correct enzyme and tyrosine is not converted into dihydroxyphenylalanine. It appears that the piece of DNA or gene responsible for controlling skin pigmentation can occur in two forms – one which can make the enzyme and the other which cannot. These two forms of DNA are said to be ***alleles***. Alleles control the same characteristic, but are alternatives of each other. In this case, the characteristic is skin pigmentation, and one allele (**A**) makes pigmented skin whilst the alternative allele (**a**) makes skin unpigmented (see Fig.3.1).

Because chromosomes occur in homologous pairs in cells, there are various combinations of alleles that are possible. The term *homozygous* is used to describe the situation where the alleles are both the same, in this case **AA** or **aa**. If the two alleles are different, in this case **Aa**, the term *heterozygous* is used.

Imagine a family tree where one grandparent was able to make the enzyme and so had pigmented skin, and the other grandparent lacked the enzyme and so was albino. Their daughter had pigmented skin and she married an albino man who was not able to make the enzyme. They had two children, one had pigmented skin and the other was an albino.

How can our understanding of meiosis help us to explain the inheritance of skin pigmentation in this family? Remember that chromosomes occur in pairs and that because of meiosis only one of a pair can occur in any one gamete. Assuming that the alleles in the grandparent with pigmented skin were the same, i.e. **AA**, the gamete must have contained a chromosome with an **A** allele. Using the same reasoning, the gamete from the other grandparent will have contained an **a** allele.

Fertilisation of these gametes will have produced an **Aa** zygote, i.e. an individual heterozygous for skin pigmentation. Because this individual has pigmented skin, the allele **A** for pigmented skin is said to be ***dominant***. The allele **a** has no influence in the heterozygote and is therefore said to be ***recessive***. The particular combination of alleles for a characteristic is called the ***genotype***. The actual appearance of the characteristic is called the ***phenotype***. In this case, the genotype of a person with pigmented skin can be **AA** or **Aa**. While the genotype of an albino has to be **aa**. So, while there are three possible genotypes, i.e. **Aa**, **AA** and **aa**, there are only two possible phenotypes, i.e. pigmented or unpigmented skin.

allele one of a number of alternative forms of a gene, each possessing a unique nucleotide sequence, only one of which can appear at a locus (the position of the gene in the DNA molecule). (IOB)

dominant the condition in which the effect of an allele is expressed in the phenotype even in the presence of an alternative (recessive) allele. (IOB)

recessive the condition in which the effect of an allele is expressed in the phenotype of a diploid organism only in the presence of another identical allele. (IOB)

genotype the genetic constitution of an organism with respect to the alleles under consideration. (IOB)

phenotype the characteristics of an individual usually resulting from the interaction between the genotype and the environment in which development occurs. (IOB)

The man whom the daughter married must have been homozygous for the recessive allele, (i.e. **aa**) and his sperm must have contained the **a** allele. The daughter's egg could have contained either an **A** allele or an **a** allele. Their child with pigmented skin was produced by the fertilisation of an egg containing the **A** allele and a sperm containing the **a** allele, whilst their albino child was produced by an egg containing the **a** allele and a sperm containing the **a** allele.

People who study genetics use simple diagrams to show how alleles are inherited. A diagram for the example given above is shown in Fig.3.2.

To check your understanding of meiosis in the case of the production of gametes in the daughter of this family, work through the diagram in Fig.3.3.

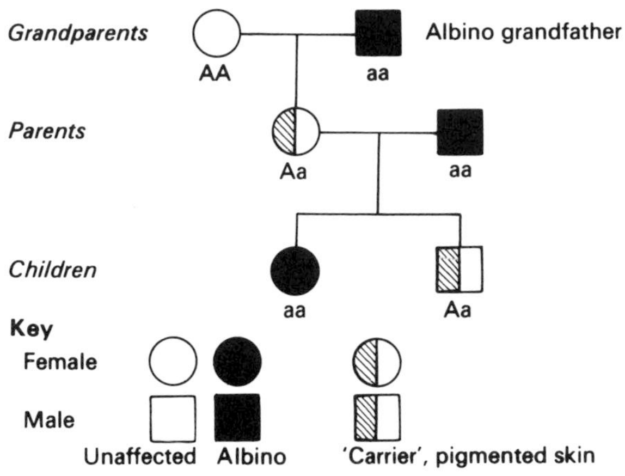

Grandparents
Albino grandfather
AA
aa
Parents
Aa
aa
Children
aa
Aa
Key
Female
Male
Unaffected
Albino
'Carrier', pigmented skin

Figure 3.2 An albino family tree

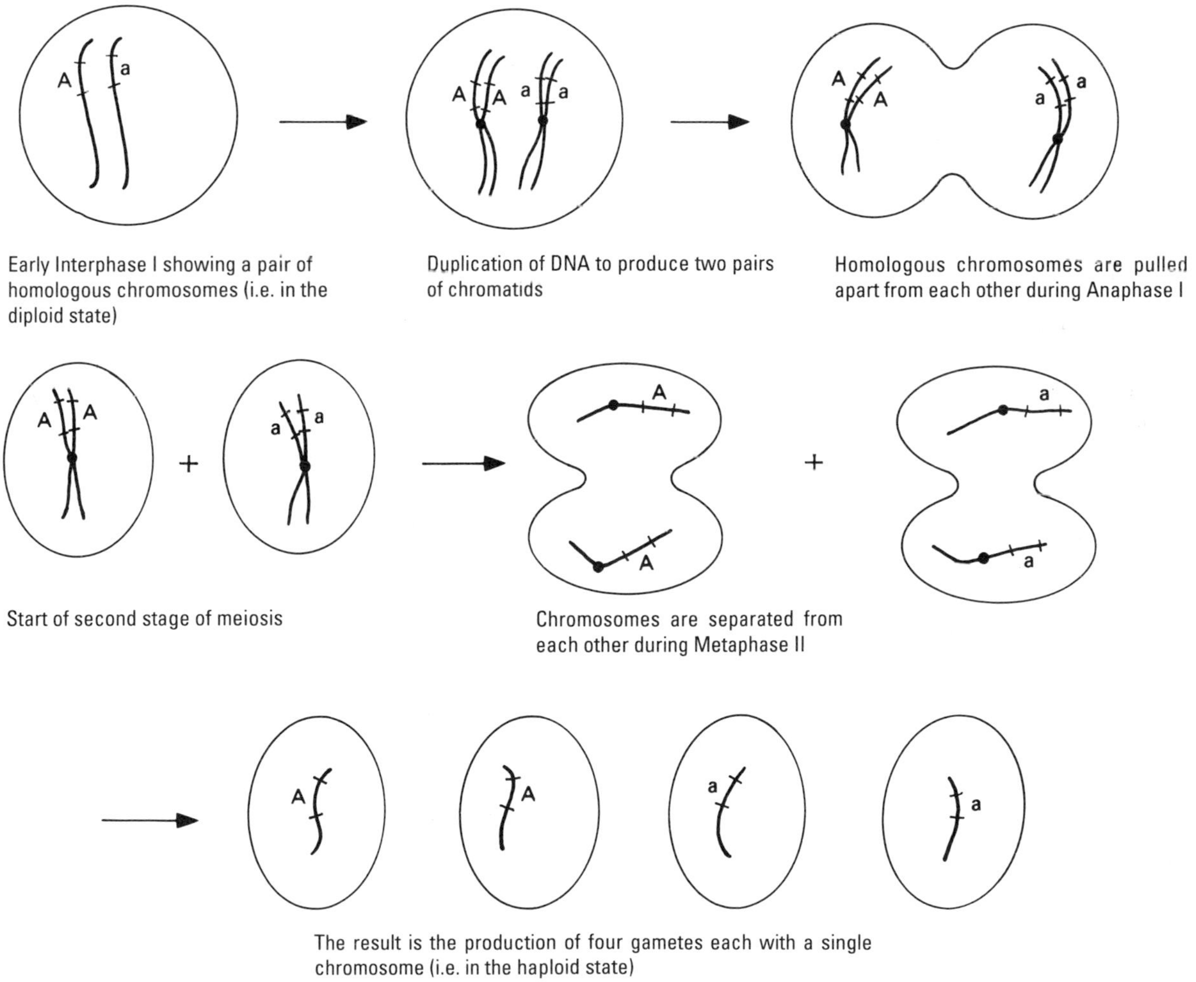

A
a
Early Interphase I showing a pair of homologous chromosomes (i.e. in the diploid state)
Duplication of DNA to produce two pairs of chromatids
Homologous chromosomes are pulled apart from each other during Anaphase I
Start of second stage of meiosis
Chromosomes are separated from each other during Metaphase II
The result is the production of four gametes each with a single chromosome (i.e. in the haploid state)

Figure 3.3 Gamete production in the Aa daughter of Figure 3.2. A = allele for pigmented skin, a = allele for unpigmented skin, i.e. albinism

INHERITED DISEASES

The diseases phenylketonuria, tyrosinosis and alkaptonuria which were mentioned earlier (page 5) are all examples of monohybrid inheritance where the sufferer is homozygous for the appropriate autosomal recessive allele. The poster shown below concerns yet another example – cystic fibrosis – the most common genetic disease in Great Britain. One child in every 2000 born can be expected to suffer from this autosomal homozygous recessive condition. One person in every 22 is a carrier of the recessive allele.

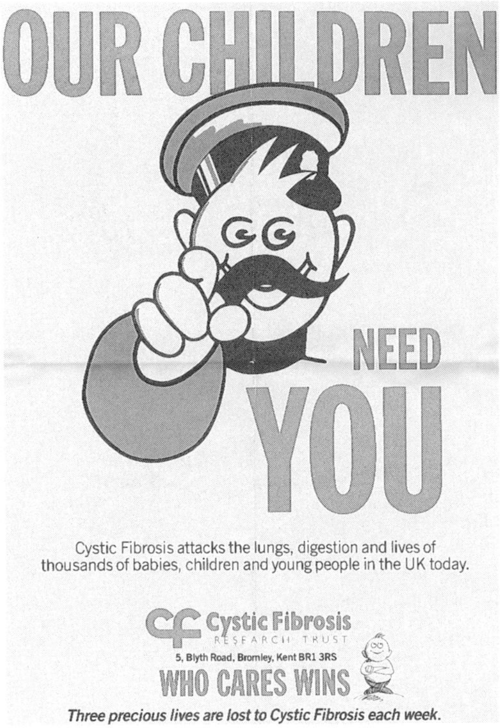
OUR CHILDREN
NEED
YOU
Cystic Fibrosis attacks the lungs, digestion and lives of thousands of babies, children and young people in the UK today.
Cystic Fibrosis
RESEARCH TRUST
5, Blyth Road, Bromley, Kent BR1 3RS
WHO CARES WINS
Three precious lives are lost to Cystic Fibrosis each week.

The normal allele allows cells in certain parts of the body to manufacture sensible amounts of mucus which is not too sticky. The recessive allele manufactures large amounts of an abnormally sticky mucus. This can have a harmful effect in those parts of the body where mucus is secreted. For example, the mucus–secreting cells in the lungs play an important part in the removal of dust and germs. In cystic children the abnormal mucus blocks the vital airways and can cause great distress with breathing. Frequent daily massage is needed to keep the airways open.

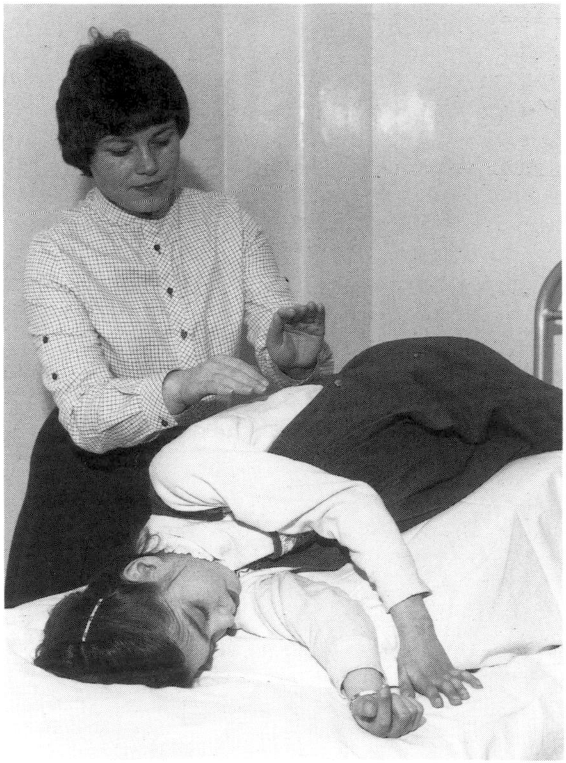

Physiotherapy treatment for a cystic fibrosis sufferer

Overproduction of mucus in the pancreas blocks the pancreatic duct and prevents the flow of digestive enzymes into the gut. Digestion is severely impaired, absorption is limited and, as a result, cystic children have large appetites to try to compensate.

The pattern of inheritance is not difficult to understand. An example of a family tree is shown in Fig.3.4. If two carriers have a child, there is a 1 in 4 chance that the child will suffer from cystic fibrosis.

Not all genetic diseases are caused by autosomal recessive alleles. Huntington's chorea is caused by an autosomal dominant allele (see Fig 3.5). The symptoms of this disease do not appear until middle age, long after the sufferer may have produced his or her own children. The disease involves a gradual deterioration of the nervous system to the extent that the adult becomes 'child-like' before inevitable death ensues.

If you look again at Figs.3.4 and 3.5, you will see that there are different ways of showing genetic crosses. A diamond is used in Fig.3.5 and this diamond will be used for all genetic crosses in this book.

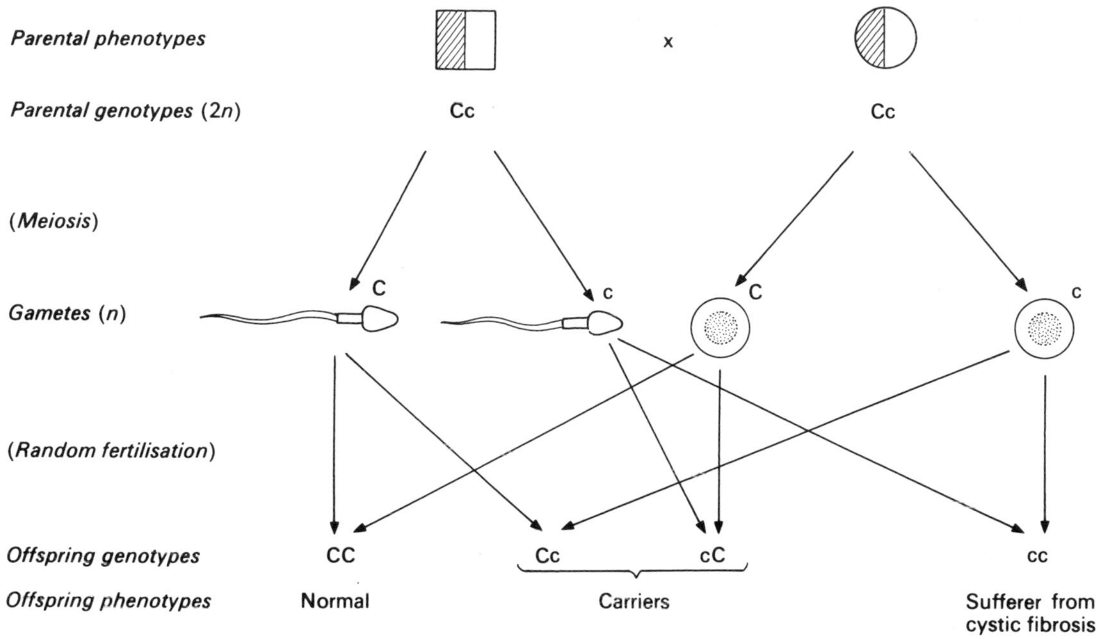
Parental phenotypes
x
Parental genotypes (2n)
Cc
Cc
(Meiosis)
Gametes (n)
C
c
C
c
(Random fertilisation)
Offspring genotypes
CC
Cc
cC
cc
Offspring phenotypes
Normal
Carriers
Sufferer from cystic fibrosis

Figure 3.4 How cystic fibrosis is inherited. C = normal allele, c = cystic fibrosis allele. Note that on average one child in four will inherit cystic fibrosis if both parents are carriers

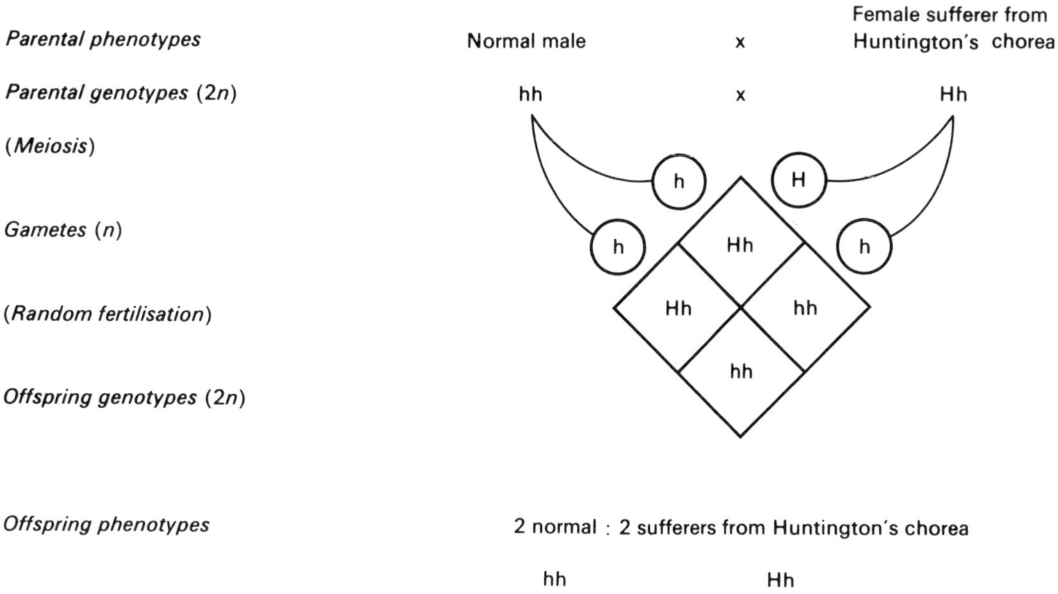
Parental phenotypes
Normal male
x
Female sufferer from Huntington's chorea
Parental genotypes (2n)
hh
x
Hh
(Meiosis)
Gametes (n)
h
h
H
h
(Random fertilisation)
Hh
Hh
hh
hh
Offspring genotypes (2n)
Offspring phenotypes
2 normal : 2 sufferers from Huntington's chorea
hh
Hh

Figure 3.5 How Huntington's chorea is inherited

'Norfolk disease' is implacable enemy

HUNTINGTON'S chorea is an implacable hereditary killer, research indicates that 7 $^1/_2$ people in 100,000 suffer from it.

The first symptoms are difficult to diagnose for certain: bursts of temper, loss of memory, physical awkwardness. The brain shrinks, bringing a slow decline into dementia, with involuntary movements building to grotesque contortions and double incontinence. Death is painful, slow, undignified and inevitable.

If everyone who has the disease in their families stopped having children, Huntington's chorea could be stamped out. But it is a desperately hard choice to make. There is a 50:50 chance of inheriting the disease, a cruel statistic made worse by the fact that it does not usually show itself until middle age; the crucial decision whether to have children must be taken before people know if they have the disease.

A BBC2 documentary focusses on one family, the Whytes, who have lived with this knowledge for three generations. "A Family Apart" took two years to make.

Mary Whyte had had four children by the time her husband, Sandy, contracted Huntington's chorea more than 30 years ago. Three of their children inherited the disease; the fourth does not know whether she has or not.

Susan developed the disease when she was only 24 and died ten years ago, leaving a daughter, Catherine.

Nick was diagnosed the year Susan died and has not much longer to live.

Simon, who has a daughter, is struggling to come to terms with the disease, after thinking that at 38 he had escaped it.

The fourth child is Prue Willday, and she has two children. Like the rest of the younger generation of the Whytes, these two children have the family question mark hanging over them.

A presymptomatic test is available providing there is enough information in the available DNA from the family. To date the actual gene has not been located and the test is dependent on a genetic marker and therefore cannot guarantee 100% accuracy. There is also a pre-natal test.

Prue Willday says she would rather live with the uncertainty than be told definitely that she will develop the disease. The test does not indicate the age the disease is likely to begin.

Prue Willday's decision to have children laid her open to criticism by some in the medical profession - describing it as selfish and immoral; she admits that it is a difficult thing to defend.

Prue's brother, Nick, and his wife, Marion, refused to take the risk. But to Prue, and to Simon, children are an integral part of being married, and half a life is better than none at all.

The longer Prue stays clear of the disease, the greater are her chances of escaping it; they have improved to 44 per cent, instead of 50 - but one of her aunts was 57 before she developed it.

"It is the worst disease in the world, a total destroyer of families. But you do not lie back and give up hope, because hope is always there."

Q

1. Read the newspaper extract, examine the genetic cross (Fig.3.5) and try to construct the family tree of the Whyte family.

2. Consider yourself in the position of Prue Willday: what would be the advantages and disadvantages of taking the test?

3. What is the earliest age that a test should be offered to members of an afflicted family?

4. Did the 'local doctor' have a point? Could the authorities make a decision to stamp out Huntington's chorea.

Modern methods making use of genetic fingerprinting, DNA probes (see page 50), and genetic advice clinics could enable people to find out if they carry an allele for an inherited disease. The information could then help them to make decisions about parenthood but it could also create ethical dilemmas.

Should everyone be made to undergo testing? Should employers and insurance companies have access to such information? Should a 'genetic register' be produced and used to prevent certain people having children? Could these ideas lead to a state-controlled system of *eugenics*? (Find out what this term means!)

There is a continuing need for research in these genetic disorders. Much of the current research is paid for by the enthusiastic efforts of charitable groups.

CHAPTER 4 MENDEL'S EXPERIMENTS

ČESKOSLOVENSKO
UNESCO
60h
G.J.MENDEL
1865-
1965
BRNO

Mendel commemorated on a Czechoslovakian postage stamp

Brno monastery

WHAT MENDEL DID

Gregor Mendel (1822–1884) was a Czechoslovakian monk. His education had been paid for by his fellow monks but sadly he did less well at University than he would have wished. He felt that he had let his brothers down and set to work in the monastery gardens at Brno. His natural curiosity lead to experiments on pea plants and by 1865 he had formulated several principles about the nature of inheritance. His work was not widely publicised or read and the full significance of what he did was not appreciated for many years.

Mendel was rather fortunate to have chosen pea plants for his studies. The flowers of the pea have a mechanism which tends to favour a large amount of self-pollination. This is the plant's insurance policy to make certain that it produces seeds. Self-pollination, however, has the disadvantage that new combinations of characteristics appear less frequently. For this reason, many pea plants tend towards homozygosity (i.e. they have pairs of the same alleles) for several of their characteristics. When Mendel chose to breed round-seeded peas with wrinkled-seeded peas, he had quite a good chance of having parents which were both homozygous. Plants which can only pass on one type of allele are said to be *pure breeding*.

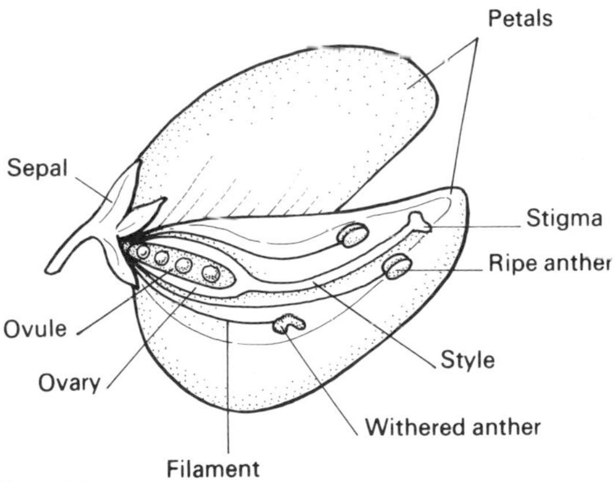
Petals
Sepal
Stigma
Ripe anther
Ovule
Style
Ovary
Withered anther
Filament

Figure 4.1

In one of his experiments, Mendel selected a pure breeding variety of pea plants which always produced round-seeded peas. He carefully opened a flower bud (*Flower A*) and removed the immature stamens (see Fig.4.2). He then selected a pure breeding wrinkled-seeded variety of pea (*Flower B*) to provide the pollen. He took the ripened stamens of the wrinkled-seeded pea plant and placed them on the stigma of the specially prepared (or emasculated) round-seeded pea flower. He covered the flower to prevent any unwanted pollination by insects and waited for the plant to produce seeds (see Fig.4.2).

It is clear that Mendel repeated this experiment many times and each time, all the seeds which were formed were round. The genetic cross of the round–seeded and wrinkled–seeded peas is shown in Fig.4.3(a).

Mendel had thought that a 'blending' might have occured and that the seeds would be either intermediate, i.e. slightly wrinkled, or else a mixture of both wrinkled and round seeds. Clearly this was not the case and an alternative hypothesis had to be made.

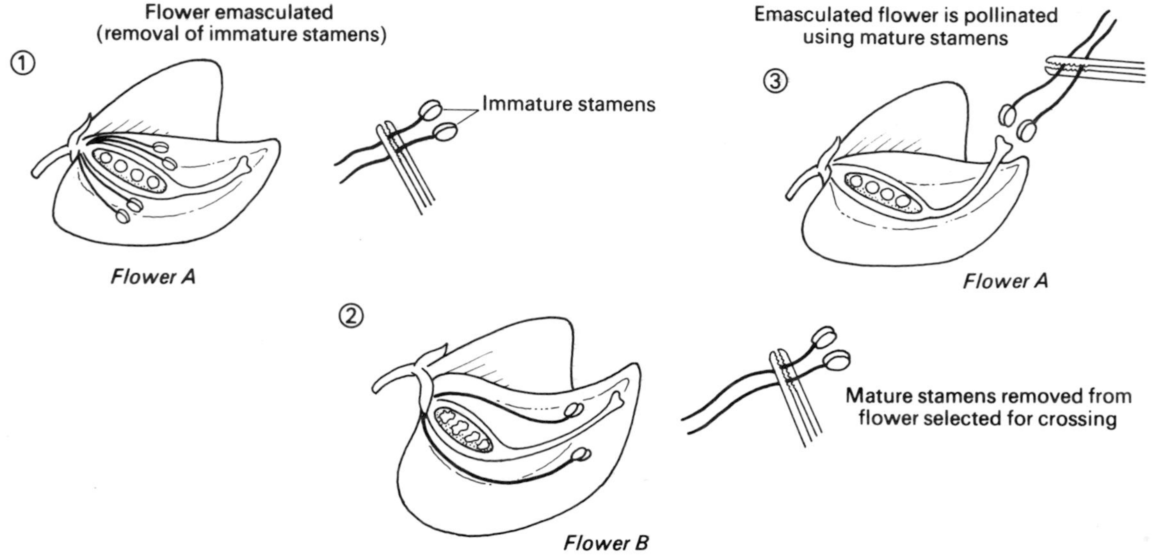

Flower emasculated
(removal of immature stamens)
①
Immature stamens
Flower A
Emasculated flower is pollinated using mature stamens
③
Flower A
②
Mature stamens removed from flower selected for crossing
Flower B

Figure 4.2 Preparation of pea flowers for Mendel's experiments

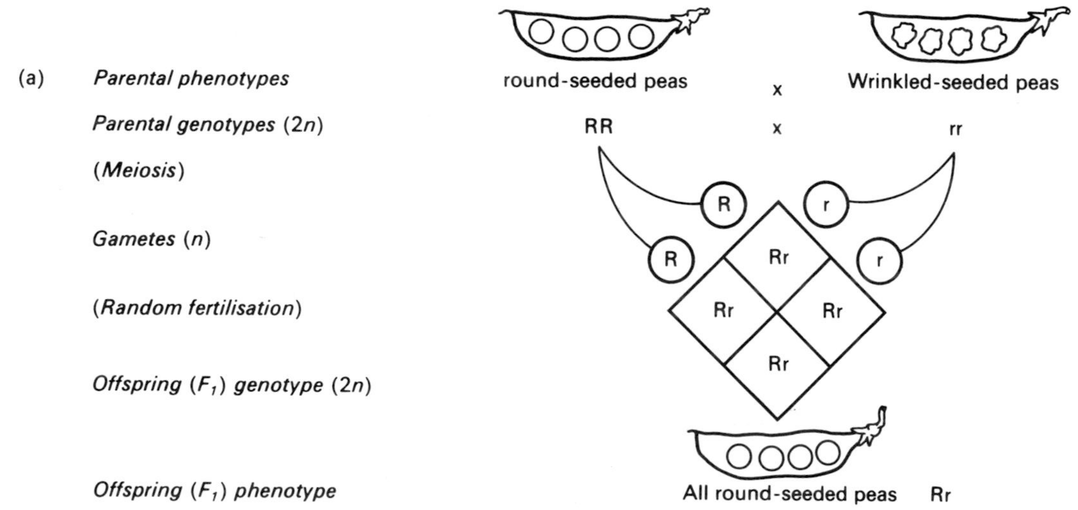

(a)
Parental phenotypes
Parental genotypes (2*n*)
(*Meiosis*)
Gametes (*n*)
(*Random fertilisation*)
Offspring (F_1) *genotype* (2*n*)
Offspring (F_1) *phenotype*
round-seeded peas
x
Wrinkled-seeded peas
RR
x
rr
R
R
r
r
Rr
Rr
Rr
Rr
All round-seeded peas
Rr

Figure 4.3(a) Mendel's cross of a round-seeded plant (homozygous dominant) with a wrinkled-seeded plant (homozygous recessive). The resulting offspring of this cross (known as the F_1 generation) were all round-seeded heterozygous plants

Mendel continued with the breeding programme. He took the round seeds produced by his experimental cross (see Fig 4.3a) and grew them. He allowed some of these plants to self-pollinate and collected the seeds of what was now the second generation. This time, both wrinkled and round seeds were produced but always with a majority of round seeds (see Fig.4.3b). He calculated the ratios of round to wrinkled seeds and found that there were approximately three round seeds produced for every wrinkled one. This ratio, although the numbers varied slightly from experiment to experiment, were so consistent that Mendel concluded that some mechanism was operating. His explanation, which he called *the particulate theory*, is now widely accepted as the foundation stone of modern genetics.

Mendel's theory assumed that characteristics are inherited as particles (we now know them as *alleles*). In the case of the peas, the round-seeded parent passed on the 'particle' which coded for round seeds, while the wrinkled-seeded parent passed on the 'particle' which coded for wrinkled seeds. The result of this cross would then have information from both parents, but the 'particles' of information did not blend or mix. Mendel suggested that the round characteristic was able to over-ride the wrinkled one (i.e. the characteristic was dominant). But, the information for wrinkled-seeds is still there, being *carried* as a 'silent' characteristic (i.e. the characteristic was *recessive*).

In the second stage of the experiment, the self-pollinated plants could pass on either wrinkled or round particles. The chance of passing on wrinkled or round was 50% in each pollen grain (or ovule). One quarter of the resulting seeds would carry only round information, one quarter would carry only wrinkled information and the remainder (a half) would carry both wrinkled and round. Since roundness is dominant, 3/4 of the seeds would be round and 1/4 would be wrinkled, consistent with Mendel's observations.

Mendel also developed a test for heterozygosity, to determine whether plants were pure breeding or not, using pure-breeding recessive plants. Using this *test cross*, Mendel was able to show that the round-seeded peas produced in the first cross between round-seeded and wrinkled-seeded plants

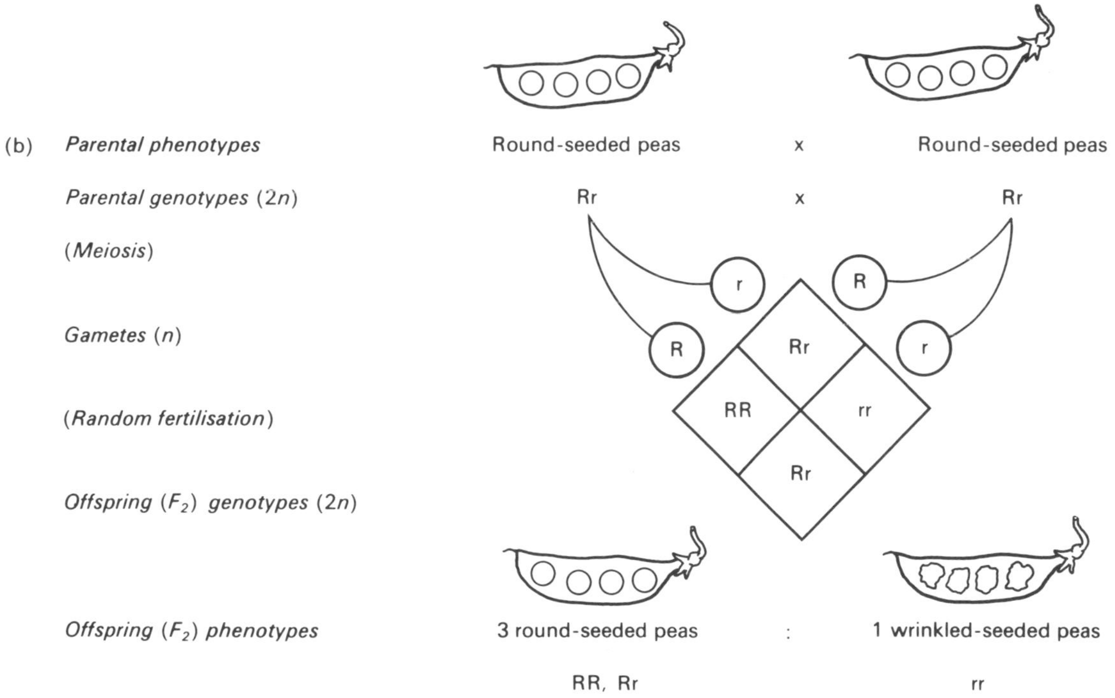

(b)
Parental phenotypes
Round-seeded peas
x
Round-seeded peas
Parental genotypes (2n)
Rr
x
Rr
(Meiosis)
r
R
Gametes (n)
R
r
(Random fertilisation)
Rr
RR
rr
Rr
Offspring (F2) genotypes (2n)
Offspring (F2) phenotypes
3 round-seeded peas
:
1 wrinkled-seeded peas
RR, Rr
rr

Figure 4.3(b) Mendel's cross of two F_1 heterozygous plants (i.e. self-pollination). The resulting offspring of this cross (known as the F_2 generation) consisted of round-seeded and wrinkled-seeded plants in a ratio of 3:1

were indeed heterozygous and contained information for both round seeds and wrinkled seeds (see Fig.4.3(c)).

Mendel applied the same principle of the particulate theory when he demonstrated that tallness in peas was dominant to dwarfness. A pure tall plant when crossed with a pure dwarf plant produced all tall offspring – but, of course, these plants were all carriers of dwarfness. In a mixture of pure tall and hybrid tall plants, it would be impossible to tell which were carriers and which were not solely on appearance. Crossing these plants with a dwarf pea plant (i.e. a test cross) would show the difference. If the tall plant was pure breeding, all the offspring would be tall; if it was a hybrid tall, 50% of the offspring would be tall and 50% would be dwarf (see Fig.4.4). Can you work this out?

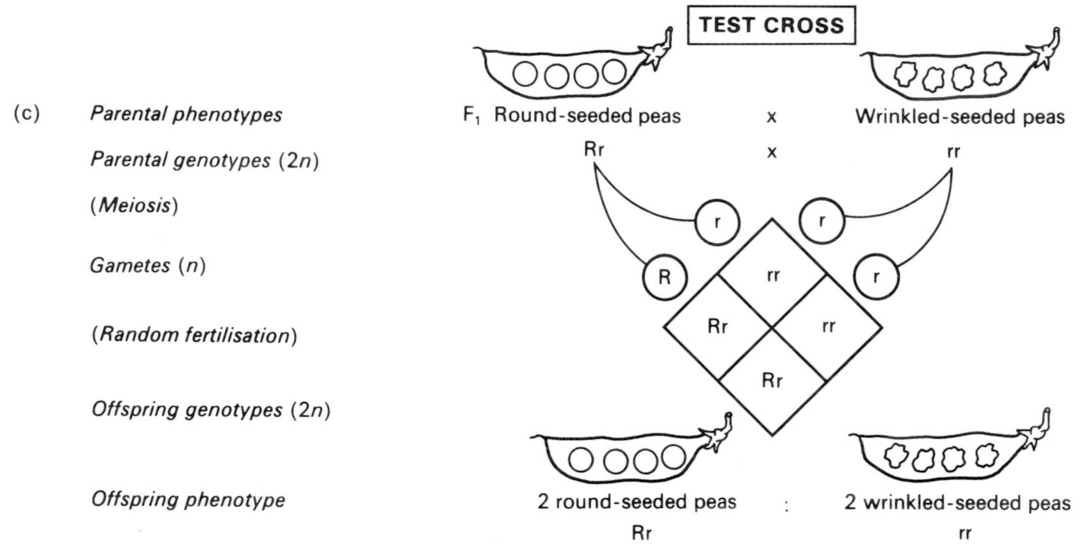
TEST CROSS
(c)
Parental phenotypes
Parental genotypes (2n)
(Meiosis)
Gametes (n)
(Random fertilisation)
Offspring genotypes (2n)
Offspring phenotype
F1 Round-seeded peas
x
Wrinkled-seeded peas
Rr
x
rr
r
r
R
r
rr
Rr
rr
Rr
2 round-seeded peas
:
2 wrinkled-seeded peas
Rr
rr

Figure 4.3(c) Test for heterozygosity

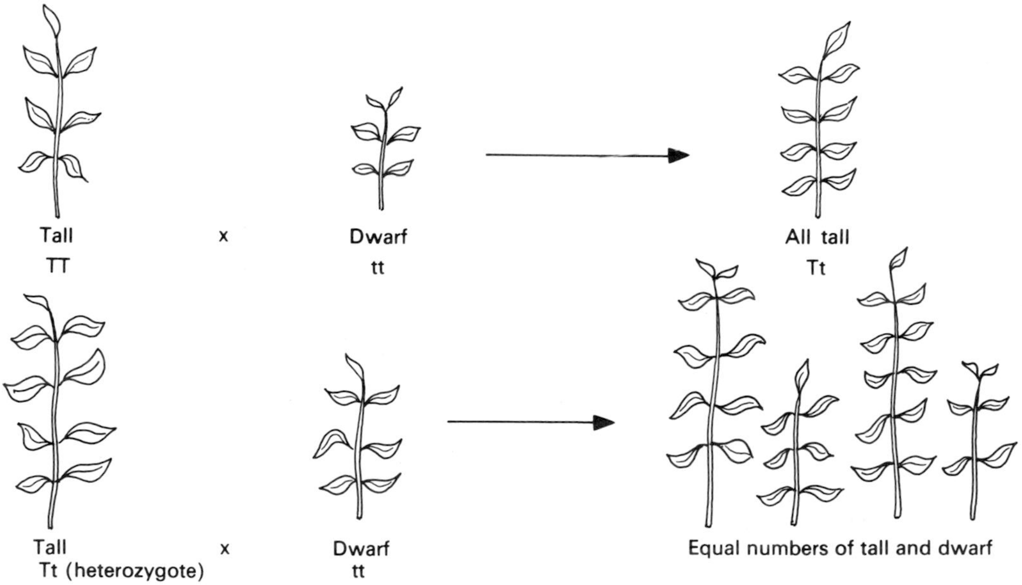
Tall
TT
x
Dwarf
tt
All tall
Tt
Tall
Tt (heterozygote)
x
Dwarf
tt
Equal numbers of tall and dwarf

Figure 4.4 Test for homozygosity (test cross) (a) A pure breeding tall plant crossed with a dwarf (homozygous recessive) plant produces all tall offspring. (b) A heterozygous tall plant crossed with a dwarf plant produces tall and dwarf plants in a ratio of 1:1

RED AND WHITE MAKES PINK – CODOMINANCE

Mendel's particulate theory was ahead of its time. No one knew of the existence of genes and Darwin's ideas about the origin of species were just being formulated. (There is no evidence that Darwin and Mendel knew of each other's works.) Mendel, with his deeply religious beliefs, doubted that something as important as inheritance could be simply decided by chance. He felt that a God could not allow such randomness and some of his results show that he sometimes made adjustments so that the ratios obeyed a 'perfect law'.

Having arrived at his theory, Mendel was to discover that some characteristics did not obey the basic rule of simple dominance and recessiveness. When investigating the inheritance of flower colour in peas, Mendel found that 'blending' could occur. Let us take an example found in some varieties of sweet pea.

Some sweet pea varieties have red flowers and others have white flowers. In both of these varieties, these colours breed true. When a red-flowered sweet pea is crossed with a white-flowered one, the offspring is neither red nor white (see Fig.4.5 (a) and (b)). In fact, all of the offspring are pink! This suggests that the allele for red flowers is not dominant, but neither is the white one. The two alleles seem to combine, or blend, to produce pink flowers. This is sometimes referred to as a *dilution* (red diluted by white = pink).

(a)

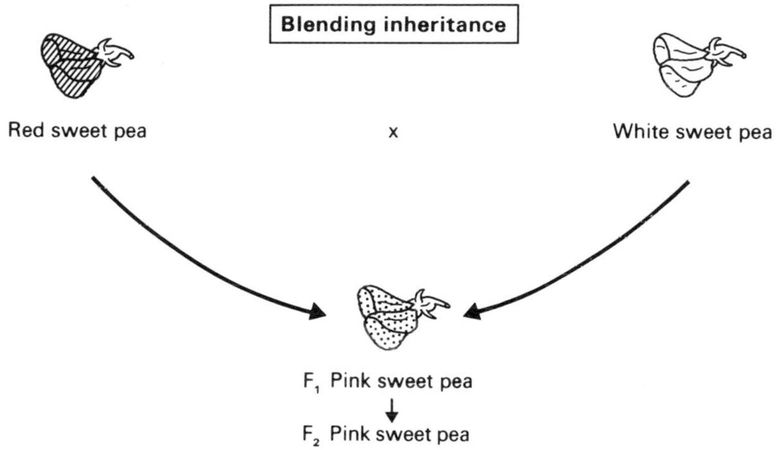
Blending inheritance
Red sweet pea
x
White sweet pea
F_1 Pink sweet pea
F_2 Pink sweet pea

(a) All F_1 offspring are pink. If the red and white characteristics 'blend' together then if a pink plant is crossed with another pink plant all the offspring should be pink

(b)

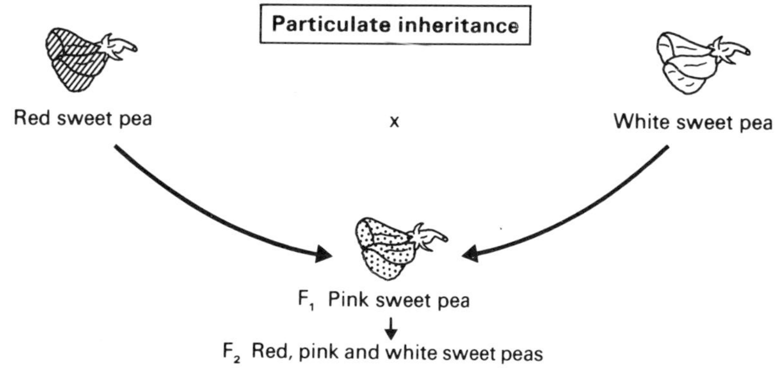
Particulate inheritance
Red sweet pea
x
White sweet pea
F_1 Pink sweet pea
F_2 Red, pink and white sweet peas

(b) All F1 offspring are pink. If the red and white characteristics are 'particles' then if a pink plant is crossed with another pink plant the red and white characteristics should reappear in new combinations

Figure 4.5 Codominance: blending versus particulate theory - Mendel's ideas

(c)

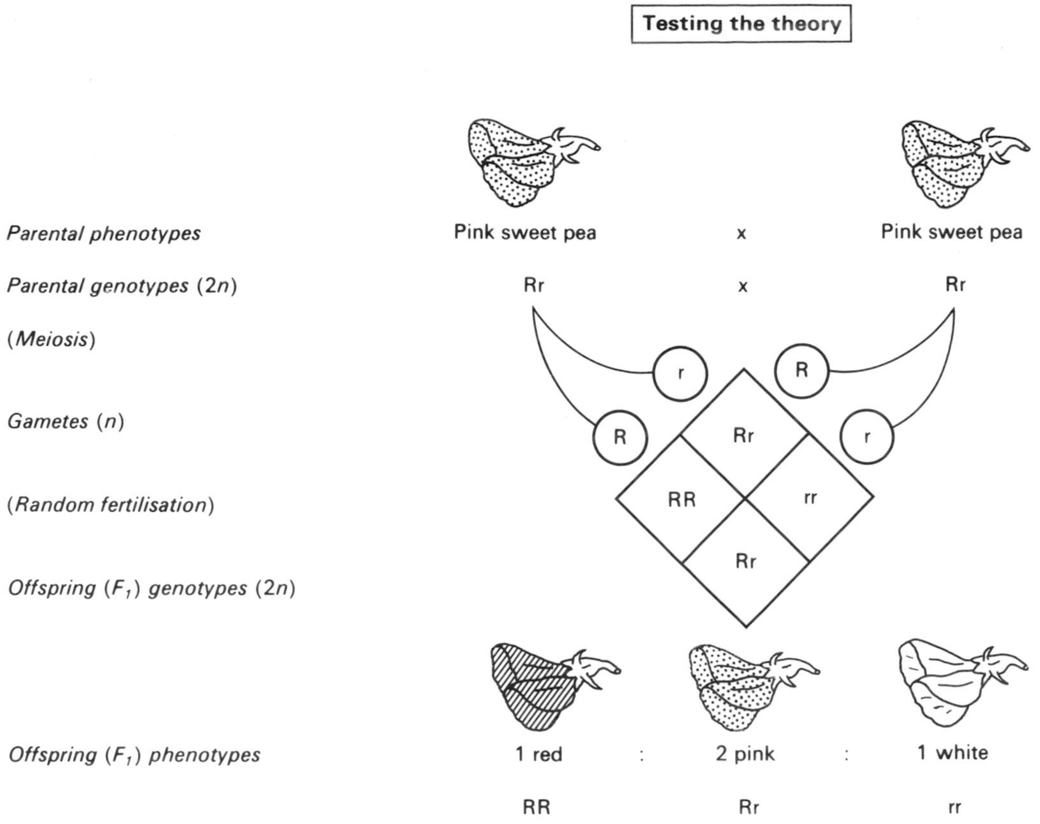

Testing the theory
Parental phenotypes
Pink sweet pea
x
Pink sweet pea
Parental genotypes (2n)
Rr
x
Rr
(Meiosis)
Gametes (n)
r
R
R
r
(Random fertilisation)
Rr
RR
rr
Rr
Offspring (F1) genotypes (2n)
Offspring (F1) phenotypes
1 red : 2 pink : 1 white
RR
Rr
rr

Figure 4.5(c) Testing the theory. When a pink plant is crossed with another pink plant the red and white characteristics have reappeared in new combinations - proving the particulate theory beyond doubt

So what happens if the pink-flowered plants are allowed to self-pollinate? A cross between two pink-flowered varieties does not produce all pink-flowered offspring. In fact, only about half of the offspring are pink, the others are red or white in roughly equal proportions (see Fig.4.5 (c)).

Q 1. Why not be a Gregor Mendel and try to work it out? Does the *particulate theory* still hold true or do you need to revise your views?

Mendel wrestled with this problem too! He came to the conclusion that his theory was still intact. The dilution was an illusion. True, when red and white information were together in the one plant, the flowers were pink, but when the pink plants were self-pollinated, the colours behaved as particles again. If they had truly blended, all the offspring would be pink (the red and white particles would now be pink particles) and red or white flowers would be impossibilities. Mendel had discovered *codominance*. When the two characteristics were together, they each had some effect and a compromise was made. In subsequent generations however, the red and white characteristics were free to express themselves again.

Mendel was one of the most careful and painstaking of all scientists, planning his experiments well and clearly recording his observations. He was able to hypothesise, and so developed a completely new branch of science (which some call Mendelism). Some historians believe that Mendel may have 'improved' his results in order to obtain ratios closer to the classic 3:1 and 9:3:3:1. However, there is no doubt that Mendel's techniques were sound and his ability to reason from his observations prepared the ground for the subsequent development of plant and animal breeding.

Q 2. Try to work out the results of crossing (a) pink sweet peas with white ones and (b) pink sweet peas with red ones. See answers on page 98.

What was true of Mendel's peas is also true of other organisms. Fig.4.6 shows a cross made between two mice. One mouse is homozygous **BB** and appears black, the other mouse is homozygous **bb** and appears brown. All of the offspring are black showing that **B** is dominant to **b**.

3. Suppose that two of the black mice produced in the cross (Fig. 4.6) were then allowed to interbreed. What do you predict will be the colours and ratios of the second generation of mice?
See answer on page 98.

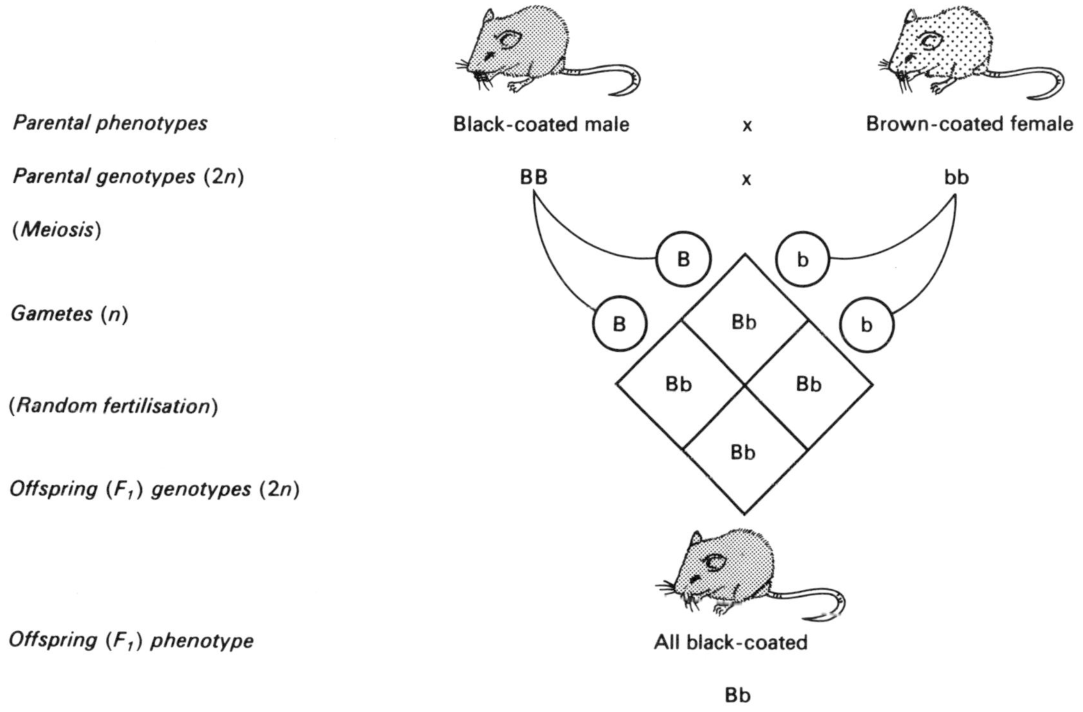
Parental phenotypes
Black-coated male
x
Brown-coated female
Parental genotypes (2n)
BB
x
bb
(Meiosis)
Gametes (n)
B
B
b
b
(Random fertilisation)
Bb
Bb
Bb
Bb
Offspring (F1) genotypes (2n)
Offspring (F1) phenotype
All black-coated
Bb

Figure 4.6 Mouse coat colour

CHAPTER 5 MENDEL'S CONTRIBUTION TO HUMAN GENETICS

INTRODUCTION

Mendel laid down the rules for determining the likely offspring of a particular cross. Until the particulate theory of inheritance was widely accepted, early attempts to improve the yield of crops or the qualities of animals were made by rather haphazard crosses. Improvements of breeds involved some selection processes but the meticulous records needed to make predictable crosses did not really exist. Darwin wrote about this process of 'artificial selection' and this led on to his later ideas on 'natural selection'.

Once it was understood that some factors could be 'masked' by others, it became possible to explain why some plants or animals with desirable characteristics often failed to pass them on to all of their offspring. This new understanding also helped to explain how novel combinations could sometimes occur when the most unlikely organisms were crossed together. Carefully planned breeding programmes have successfully incorporated such features as disease resistance, rapid ripening, high yield and hardiness to extremes of climate into many economically important crop plant species.

The direct benefits of DNA research to humans are increasing daily. Over 4000 different harmful genes in people have been described and identified. A project to identify the precise nature of the entire *human genome* is underway (see Page 86). This project has been described as the biological equivalent of putting the first man on the moon. In truth it is probably even more ambitious than that! Genetic counsellors can now examine the family trees of people who are at risk of passing on a genetic disorder and, using Mendel's laws, they are able to assess the probabilities of a future child inheriting the disorder. There are several quite common recessive traits which may severely affect the health of an affected person. Some examples of recessive and dominant traits are shown in Table 5.1.

HUMAN CARRIERS

Mendel's concept of a *carrier* explains why two apparently healthy parents can have a child suffering from something as harmless as colour blindness, or as serious as sickle cell anaemia.

About one in ten people of African or Afro-Caribbean origin are carriers of sickle cell anaemia and one in four of the children born to two carriers is likely to suffer from this disease (see Fig.5.1(a)). In Africa, carriers of sickle cell anaemia seem to gain some protection from malaria, so it is potentially

Recessive	Dominant
Widow's peak hairline	High convex nose bridge (to straight or concave)
Tasting PTU (phenylthiourea) 'bitter taste of grapefruit'	Brachydactyly, i.e. very short fingers or toes
Attached ear lobes	Long ears (to short)
Sickle cell trait	Dimple in chin (to no dimple)
Thalassaemia	Freckles
Rhesus blood group	Huntington's chorea
Phenylketonuria	
Cystic fibrosis	

Table 5.1 Monohybrid characteristics in humans

advantageous to be a carrier. The homozygous recessive sufferers from sickle cell anaemia however are at a severe disadvantage. Their red blood cells have an abnormal shape and do not carry oxygen efficiently. The red blood cells also tend to stick together and so interfere with the blood flow in the capillaries. This often causes severe pain in the joints and abdomen.

Using genetic counselling, it is also possible to predict the likelihood of another illness affecting the structure of the haemoglobin in the red blood cells. This illness is called thalassaemia and like sickle cell anaemia it is a recessive trait. It affects one in four of the children born to two carriers of the disease.

Look carefully at Fig.5.1 (b) and answer the following questions.

Q 1. B has thalassalemia. Explain why none of her children have the disease.

2. Explain why although F and G are healthy their son, I, has thalassaemia.

3. A genetic counsellor explains to F and G that their chance of having another baby with thalassaemia is one in four. So they are certain that their next baby will be healthy. Should they be?

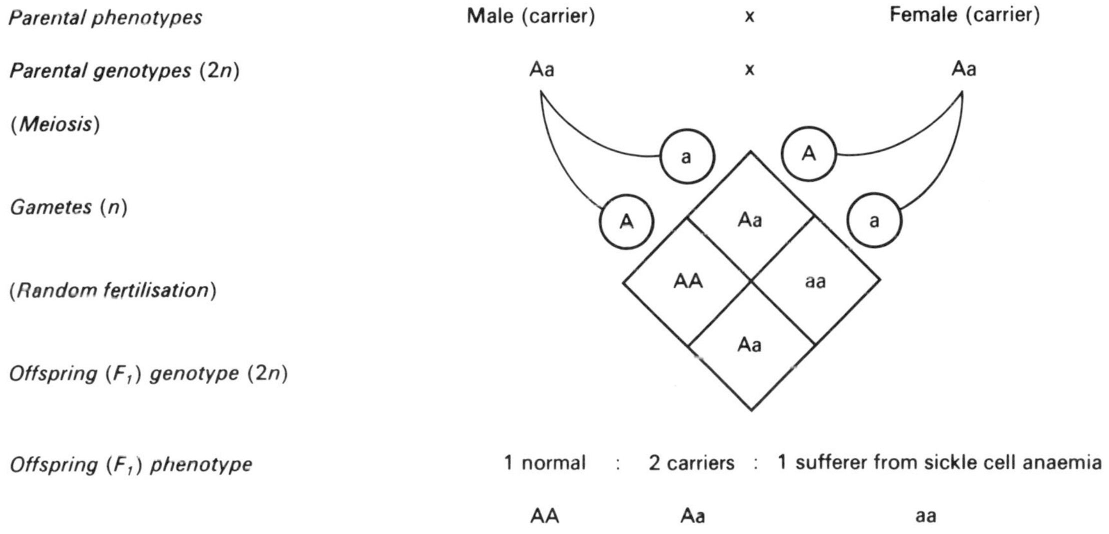

Parental phenotypes
Male (carrier) x Female (carrier)
Parental genotypes (2*n*)
Aa x Aa
(*Meiosis*)
Gametes (*n*)
a
A
A
a
(*Random fertilisation*)
Aa
AA
aa
Aa
Offspring (F_1) *genotype* (2*n*)
Offspring (F_1) *phenotype*
1 normal : 2 carriers : 1 sufferer from sickle cell anaemia
AA
Aa
aa

Figure 5.1(a) A genetic cross between two carriers of sickle cell anaemia. A = normal allele, a = sickle cell allele

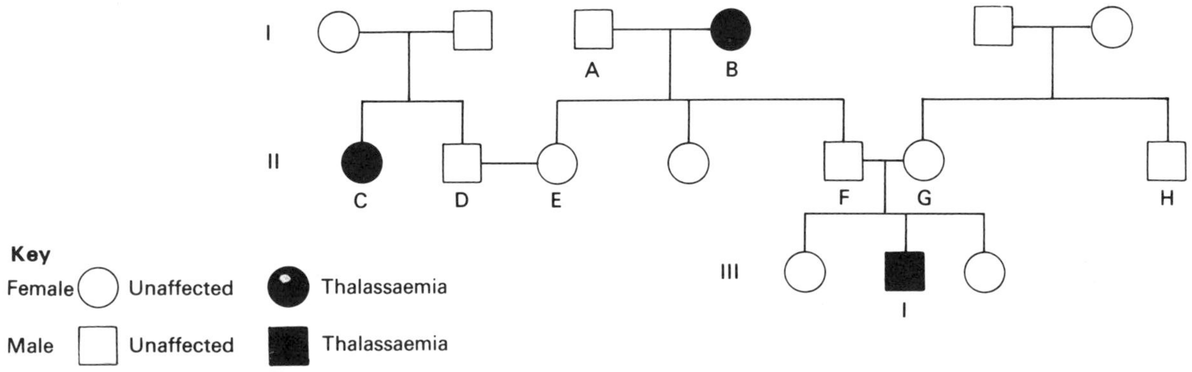

I
A
B
II
C
D
E
F
G
H
III
I
Key
Female
Unaffected
Thalassaemia
Male
Unaffected
Thalassaemia

Figure 5.1(b) A family tree of thalassaemia sufferers

SEX DETERMINATION AND SEX LINKAGE

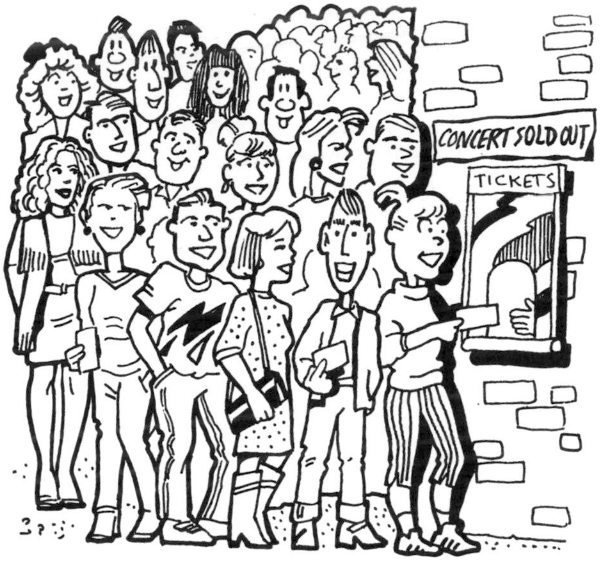
CONCERT SOLD OUT
TICKETS

If you count the number of boys and girls in the picture above you will see that the number of boys is similar to the number of girls. This 50:50 ratio may not come as a surprise to you, but why does it exist? If you have understood meiosis you ought to be able to work out the answer for yourself.

During meiosis the sex chromosomes behave in the same way as the autosomes. The diagrams in Fig. 5.2 show what happens to the sex chromosomes during the meiotic cell division of a cell from the male testis (which makes the male gametes) and a cell from the female ovary (which makes the female gametes).

As you can see, all of the female gametes contain an **X** chromosome, but only half of the male gametes contain an **X** chromosome, the other half contain a **Y** chromosome. The sex of the offspring will be determined by whichever type of male gamete (i.e. sperm) is involved with fertilisation of the female gamete (i.e. ova). If it is a **Y**-bearing sperm, the child will be male. If it is an **X**-bearing sperm, the child will be female.

The theory suggests that a sex ratio of 1:1 might be expected. In practice this ratio is only observed among ten-year-olds. At conception, the ratio is about 114 males to 100 females. Different mortality rates of the embryos produce a ratio of about 106 males to 100 females at birth. In older age groups males are more prone to mortality and so the number of females exceeds the number of males.

SO YOU THINK THAT YOU UNDERSTAND HOW SEX IS INHERITED?

For the vast majority of cases it is the XX or XY story. However we now learn that there is one major gene (SRY - the male-determining factor) that is found near the end of the Y chromosome. Its job is to cause the gonads to develop into testes and to push the fetus towards maleness. In its absence the fetus develops into a girl baby. At meiosis in the testis the X and Y chromosomes form a homologous pair. They separate at anaphase I and form four haploid sperms - two carrying X and two carrying Y. However, what sometimes happens is that crossing over (see p68) occurs and the end of a Y chromatid can become attached to an X chromatid. This means that the X chromatid would carry the male-determining factor and the Y chromatid would not. So there are some cases emerging of XX males and XY females. Confusing isn't it?

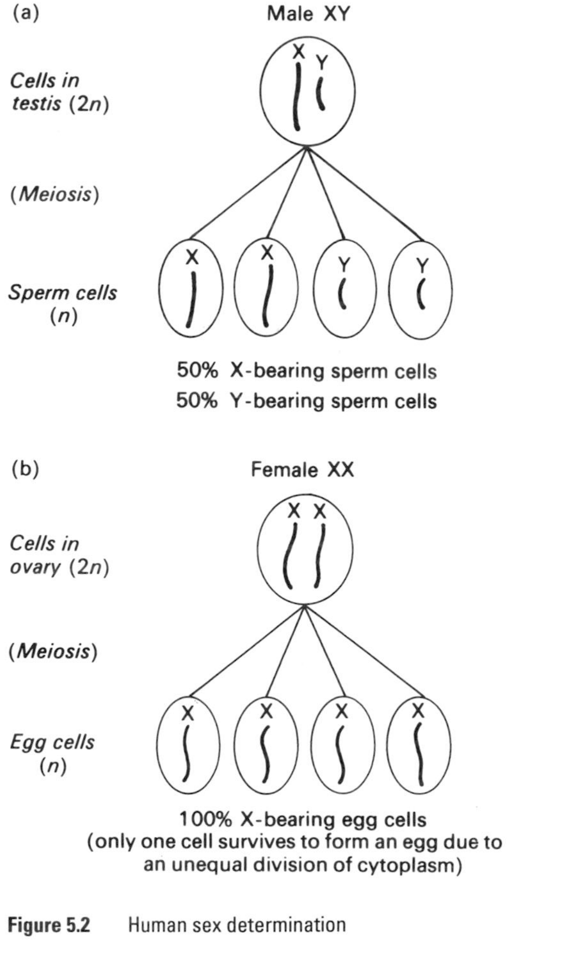
(a)
Male XY
Cells in testis (2n)
X Y
(Meiosis)
Sperm cells (n)
X X Y Y
50% X-bearing sperm cells
50% Y-bearing sperm cells
(b)
Female XX
Cells in ovary (2n)
X X
(Meiosis)
Egg cells (n)
X X X X
100% X-bearing egg cells
(only one cell survives to form an egg due to an unequal division of cytoplasm)

Figure 5.2 Human sex determination

Many silly stories exist about sex determination. The ancient Incas of Peru lived in the Andes mountains where it was thought that heavy breathing to obtain sufficient oxygen created alkaline body fluids. This was thought to favour the survival of **X**-bearing sperm to the extent that there was an excess of girl children. To get round this problem the Incas had mating races, during which it was thought that the lactic acid build-up in the bodies of the women while running favoured the survival of **Y**-bearing sperm and hence encouraged production of boy children – assuming the men could catch the women!

The genes which determine sex are carried on the sex chromosomes. There are some genes for other characteristics which are also carried on the sex chromosomes. The two best known examples are the genes for red-green colour blindness and the gene for haemophilia, a disease in which the blood fails to clot properly. Another less well known example is the gene for one form of muscular dystrophy. Because these genes are found on the sex chromosomes they tend to be passed on with those genes determining sex and so are called *sex-linked* genes.

In the three examples mentioned it is the recessive allele which causes the problem. Both the recessive allele and the normal allele are only found on the **X** chromosome. This is because the **Y** chromosome is not long enough to have a corresponding place or *locus* for all of the alleles found on the **X** chromosome. A woman can carry the recessive allele on one of her **X** chromosomes and not suffer the disease providing her other **X** chromosome has the normal allele. Such women are said to be *carriers*. Since a man only has one **X** chromosome, if he has the recessive allele he has no choice but to suffer the disease.

Figure 5.3 explains the theoretical pattern of inheritance when a female carrier of red-green colour blindness marries a normal male. As expected, half the offspring are female and half are male. What is interesting is that none of the female offspring will suffer colour blindness, although half of them can be expected to be carriers. This contrasts with the male offspring where half can be expected to be normal while the other half can be expected to suffer colour blindness.

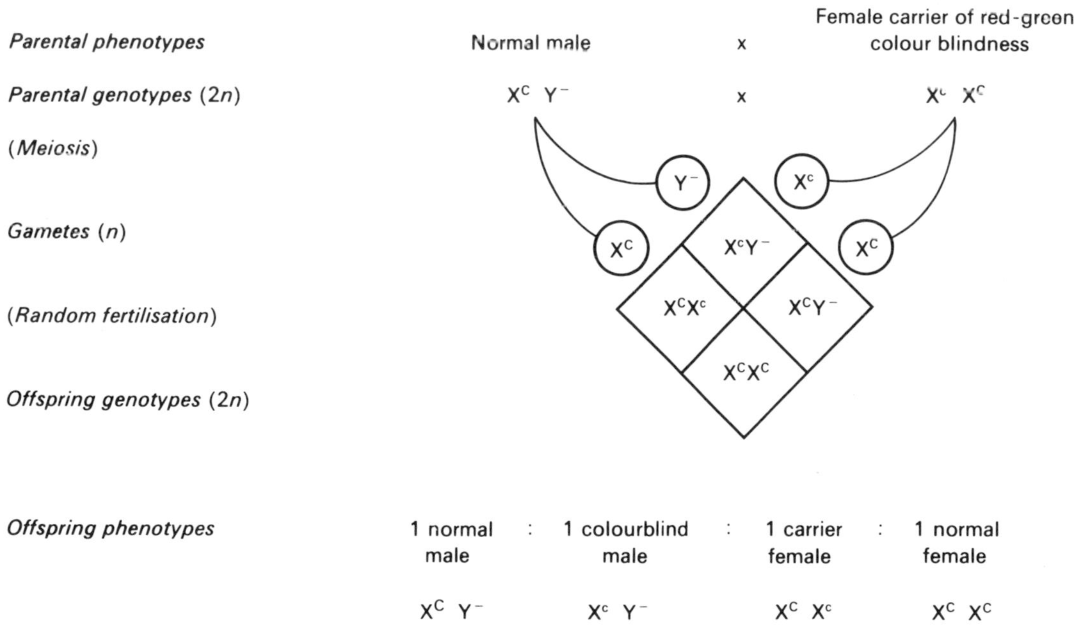

Parental phenotypes
Normal male
x
Female carrier of red-green colour blindness
Parental genotypes (2n)
X^C Y^-
x
X^c X^C
(Meiosis)
Gametes (n)
Y^-
X^C
X^c
X^C
(Random fertilisation)
X^cY^-
X^CX^c
X^CY^-
X^CX^C
Offspring genotypes (2n)
Offspring phenotypes
1 normal male : 1 colourblind male : 1 carrier female : 1 normal female
X^C Y^-
X^c Y^-
X^C X^c
X^C X^C

Figure 5.3 The inheritance of red-green colour blindness. X^C - allele for normal vision, X^c = allele for colour blindness

Queen Victoria's family

Queen Victoria is the most famous example of a carrier of the disease haemophilia. Her marriage to Prince Albert and the subsequent family tree reveals how the recessive allele was passed on to some of the other Royal Houses of Europe. Three of her daughters are known to have been carriers (including the mother of Alexandra the wife of Czar Nicholas of Russia and at least one son (Leopold of Albany) was a haemophiliac. But Edward VII, King of Britain, carried the normal allele.

The blood of haemophiliacs is unable to clot because the recessive allele cannot bring about the manufacture of Factor VIII, a vital protein in the blood clotting process. The problem is so severe that very few males used to live long enough to father children.

Nowadays, it has become possible to inject haemophiliacs with Factor VIII extracted from donated blood supplies. They then live a normal life. Sadly, for some haemophiliacs, the blood supplies used to prepare their Factor VIII were, at one time, not screened properly for the human immunodeficiency virus (HIV) which is responsible for the onset of AIDS. This has led to a number of haemophiliacs becoming infected with this deadly virus. It is hoped that the progress being made by genetic engineering will prevent the need to use donated blood supplies to obtain Factor VIII in future. Needless to say, in the meantime, all donated blood is now screened for HIV.

■ MORE SEX-RELATED ISSUES

The problems associated with sex-linked conditions have led to an intensive study of the sex-chromosomes of humans. These chromosomes have now been *mapped* so that the positions of potentially harmful sex-linked genes are known. Geneticists and molecular biologists have pooled their knowledge to develop tests which can predict the risk of a genetic defect occurring. Screening of high-risk embryos may offer hope to couples who want to have children, but who want to avoid the tragedy of a severely handicapped baby. In the specific case of sex-linked diseases, it is possible to determine the sex of an embryo and only implant female embryos into the mother so that the risk of disease is minimal. Techniques like the one described in Fig.5.4 make use of the fact that all of the cells in an early embryo will contain the same genetic material. One long term problem associated with this technique, however, is the possibility of increasing the frequency of carriers in the population.

There are moral and legal implications of embryo testing. Embryos are after all unique individuals, even if they are at a very early stage of development. Destroying an embryo (e.g. abortion) is destroying life. Many people feel that it is the poorer quality of life which an organism might lead that sometimes justifies an early termination.

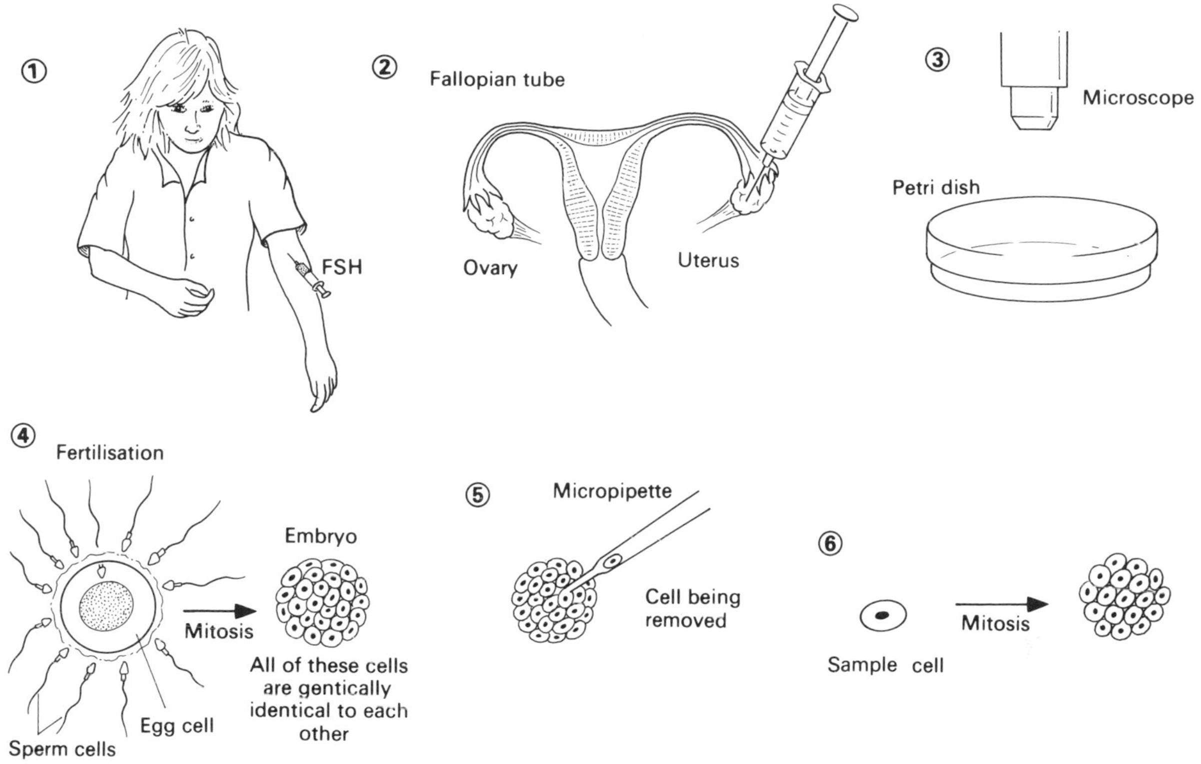
①
FSH
②
Fallopian tube
Ovary
Uterus
③
Microscope
Petri dish
④
Fertilisation
Embryo
Mitosis
All of these cells are gentically identical to each other
Egg cell
Sperm cells
⑤
Micropipette
Cell being removed
⑥
Sample cell
Mitosis

1. A woman is given an injection of follicle stimulating hormone (FSH) to promote the development of ripe ova
2. Eggs are collected using laparoscopy (i.e. fibre optic cable is used to locate the ripe ova which are then removed by syringe)
3. Eggs are mixed with sperm and observed to check that fertilisation has taken place successfully
4. Several fertilised eggs are allowed to develop into a ball of cells (the early embryo)
5. A sample cell is removed from each embryo using a micropipette. The embryo is then frozen and stored
6. The sample cell, however, is allowed to continue cell division until it produces sufficient cells for testing. The ball of cells is tested either by using a gene probe or by allowing the DNA to replicate many times so that faults can be found (see page 83). If the cells are found to be normal, the embryo from which the sample cell was taken is thawed and inserted into the woman's fallopian tube (or high in the uterus) when the woman's menstrual cycle is primed for implantation
7. Nine months later a healthy baby!

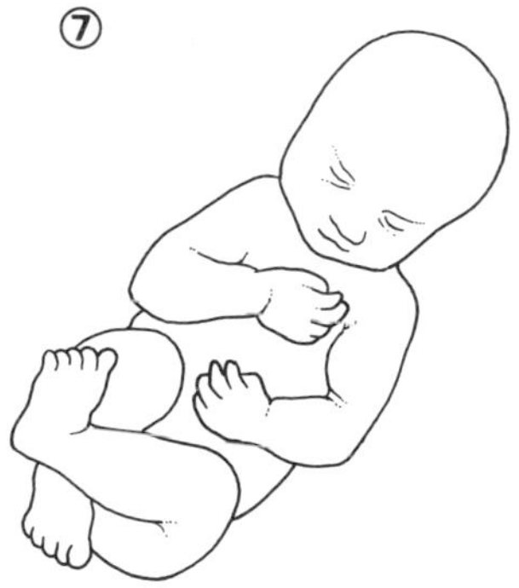
⑦

Figure 5.4 Embryo testing

The stages of embryo testing are shown above. In stage 4 a single cell is removed from the early embryo and encouraged to grow in an artificial medium. Meanwhile, the original embryo is frozen and stored. When the sample cell has divided many times, genetic tests using *DNA probes* can show whether or not the original embryo is likely to be abnormal. In this way, only normal embryos are re-introduced into the mother for their continued development.

DNA PROBES

A DNA probe is a chemical which is able to recognise a short section of DNA by joining with a specific sequence of bases. A length of 'faulty DNA' can therefore be identified enabling specific genetic deformities to be detected at an early stage.

PCR TECHNIQUES

PCR is short for *polymerase chain reaction* and is a technique which is sometimes called the 'DNA photocopier'. It enables millions upon millions of copies of DNA to be made from a very small sample. A few cells will provide enough starter material for the PCR technique to produce enough DNA for genetic fingerprinting. The technique works even on tiny amounts of non-living tissue. The most amazing example of this occured after some Manchester researchers had studied and preserved post-mortem tissue from a sailor who had died in 1959. They were intrigued to read about his symptoms prior to death which were similar to those seen in terminally ill AIDS patients. (The first description of AIDS was published as late as 1981.) The PCR technique was performed on 30-year-old autopsy material and showed that the sailor had, in fact, died from full blown AIDS. This makes it the earliest known case of AIDS in Britain by more than 20 years.

GENETIC FINGERPRINTING

This is a technique (more commonly called DNA profiling) which is used for identifying particular sections of DNA. It involves using a type of separation known as gel electrophoresis in which particular pieces of DNA move at different rates through the gel. Faulty sections of DNA can be detected as specific bands across the gel.

The curious case of cats and moths

In humans, females are said to be the homogametic sex (i.e. they have two **X** chromosomes) and males the heterogametic sex (i.e. they have one **X** and one **Y** chromosome). Since females can only pass on an **X** chromosome, they play no part in sex determination. A male is formed when a **Y**-bearing sperm fertilises an egg. When King Henry VIII blamed his various wives for their failure to produce a son, he ought to have blamed his own sperm!

Some animals reverse the sexual roles and the male is homogametic and the females are heterogametic. Butterflies and birds for example have homogametic males and heterogametic females.

The body colour of cats and magpie moths is determined by a sex-linked gene attached to the **X** chromosome. In both cases, the darker body colour is dominant to the lighter body colour.

Look at the crosses shown below. They should give you sufficient information to decide whether it is the male or the female which is homogametic in each case.

a) **Cat** (black coat dominant to yellow coat)

Parental phenotypes

Black male x Yellow female

Offspring phenotypes

2 yellow males : 2 black females

b) **Magpie moth** (dark body colour dominant to pale body colour)

Parental phenotypes

Pale male x Dark female

Offspring phenotypes

2 dark males : 2 pale females

A Fishy tale

An interesting aside about sex determination comes from the fish-farming industry. Salmon for fish farming are bred from populations obtained from different rivers. This results in the farmed fish developing a 'loss of identity'. In the wild, salmon usually return from the sea to the river in which they hatched. The characteristics which allow them to survive in this river seem to be genetically determined. However, farmed fish are selected for different characteristics such as high growth rate, tolerance of crowding and disease resistance. If these fish escape from the fish farm, they may breed with the wild salmon. By doing this, the farmed fish will tend to pass on their 'loss of identity' (as well as high growth rate, etc) so that their offspring may fail to navigate their way back to their 'parental' river. Since there are inevitably escapees from fish farms, care must be taken to reduce the risk of 'damaging' the wild population.

If only a few farmed salmon escape, then the chance of them mating with a wild salmon will be greater than that of finding another escapee with which to mate with. This is likely to result in damage to the wild population. This problem has been solved using some ingenious techniques. The aim of fish farming is to produce large fish prior to sexual maturity. Male salmon mature quickly (so as a result they do not grow very big). For this reason, fish farmers prefer bigger, female fish. Female salmon have two **X** chromosomes but their sex is actually determined by hormone levels. An excess of male hormones makes an **XX** female functionally male. Similarly, an excess of female hormone makes an **XY** male functionally female! It is possible to feed salmon a hormone supplement in their diet and so determine their sex.

Unfertilised eggs and sperm have the haploid number of chromosomes while fertilised eggs have the diploid number. If a thermal shock (a sudden rise in temperature) is given to unfertilised eggs, their chromosome number doubles. Using a similar treatment, newly fertilised eggs can be produced which are triploid (a triploid cell has three sets of chromosomes). Triploid fish are sterile and do not breed (but they taste just as good!) so if they escape the genetic damage to wild population is limited (see Fig.5.5).

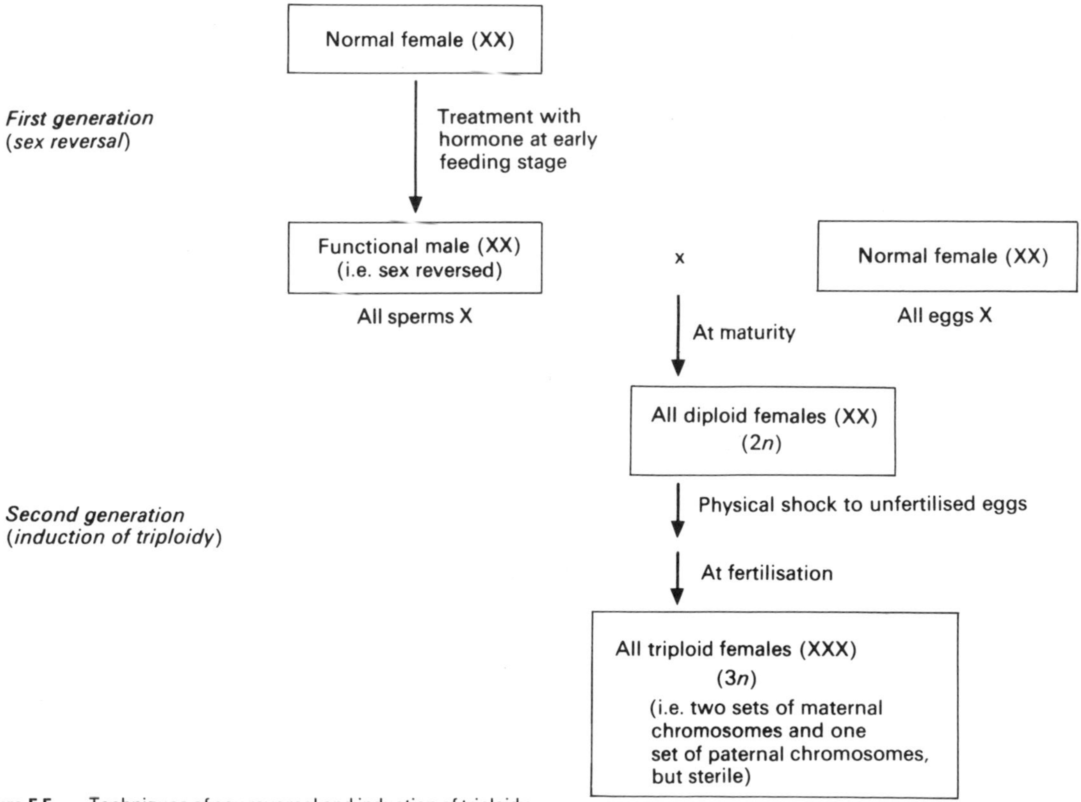
Normal female (XX)
First generation
(sex reversal)
Treatment with hormone at early feeding stage
Functional male (XX)
(i.e. sex reversed)
All sperms X
x
Normal female (XX)
All eggs X
At maturity
All diploid females (XX)
(2n)
Second generation
(induction of triploidy)
Physical shock to unfertilised eggs
At fertilisation
All triploid females (XXX)
(3n)
(i.e. two sets of maternal chromosomes and one set of paternal chromosomes, but sterile)

Figure 5.5 Techniques of sex reversal and induction of triploidy are used to produce sterile female fish for fish farming

TABOO

It may be hard to believe, but brother-sister matings were the rule among the Pharoahs of ancient Egypt. Such a phenomenon is rare in history. Indeed, a relationship between very close relatives is generally frowned upon and is a taboo that is present in many cultures. No doubt there are many reasons for this, and one of them most certainly is biological.

Individuals who have a common ancestor a few generations back may have an increased risk of producing offspring with a genetic disease. Each may possess a (recessive) genetic trait which has a greater probability of becoming combined (i.e. homozygous) in their offspring.

In the diagram shown in Fig.5.6 a girl has been born with a genetic disease. Her great grandfather was a carrier of the autosomal recessive allele known to cause the genetic disease when in the homozygous state. He appeared normal because the dominant allele was also present, but he was a carrier. The recessive allele was passed on to both his children (i.e. the girl's grandparents). Each grandparent married a normal spouse and each couple had a child (i.e. the girls parents). Both the parents appeared normal but were carriers and it was their child who was born with the disease.

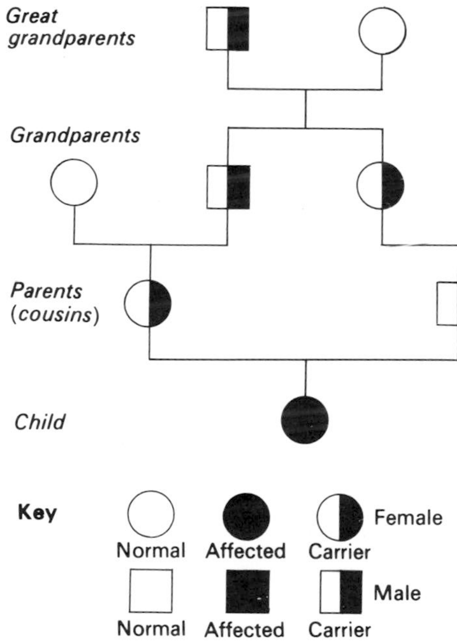

Great grandparents
Grandparents
Parents (cousins)
Child
Key
Female
Normal
Affected
Carrier
Male
Normal
Affected
Carrier

Figure 5.6 Consanguineous breeding diagram

The gene in question could be any which is inherited in the normal autosomal way, for example phenylketonuria. The point to note is that there is an increased chance of the disease appearing in children with a family tree showing very close relationships, particularly first cousin marriages. It is also possible to work out the mathematical probability of such an event. However, it must be stressed that the issue is one of probability – there is also a chance that genetic disease will *not* manifest itself as a result of such marriages. Despite the apparent intense inbreeding of the Pharoahs many of their children seemed to be normal.

WHEN MEIOSIS GOES WRONG

Aneuploidy

In Chapter 2 it was stated that the process of reduction division (i.e. meiosis) occured to produce haploid gametes. There are, however, times when this division goes wrong and the gametes do not have the exact haploid number of chromosomes. One error of this type occurs in the formation of eggs when *non-disjunction* (or non-separation) of the sex chromosomes occurs. The **X** chromosomes pair up in the early stage of cell division and then both migrate to the same pole (instead of to opposite poles). This results in some eggs containing two **X** chromosomes (**XX**) whilst other eggs contain no sex chromosomes (**O**). If an organism has an extra chromosome (or lacks one), the condition is known as *aneuploidy*.

When humans have odd numbers of sex chromosomes, their phenotypes are often affected. A summary of these effects is listed in Table 5.2.

There are dangers associated with drawing conclusions about males with **XYY** sex chromosomes (i.e. 'supermales') and their possible link with violence. A study in America, carried out on violent criminals (e.g. rapists and murderers) showed that many of these criminals had **XYY** body cells. This suggested that boys with the **XYY** condition might grow up into violent members of society. Other studies, however, have suggested that this may not be the case.

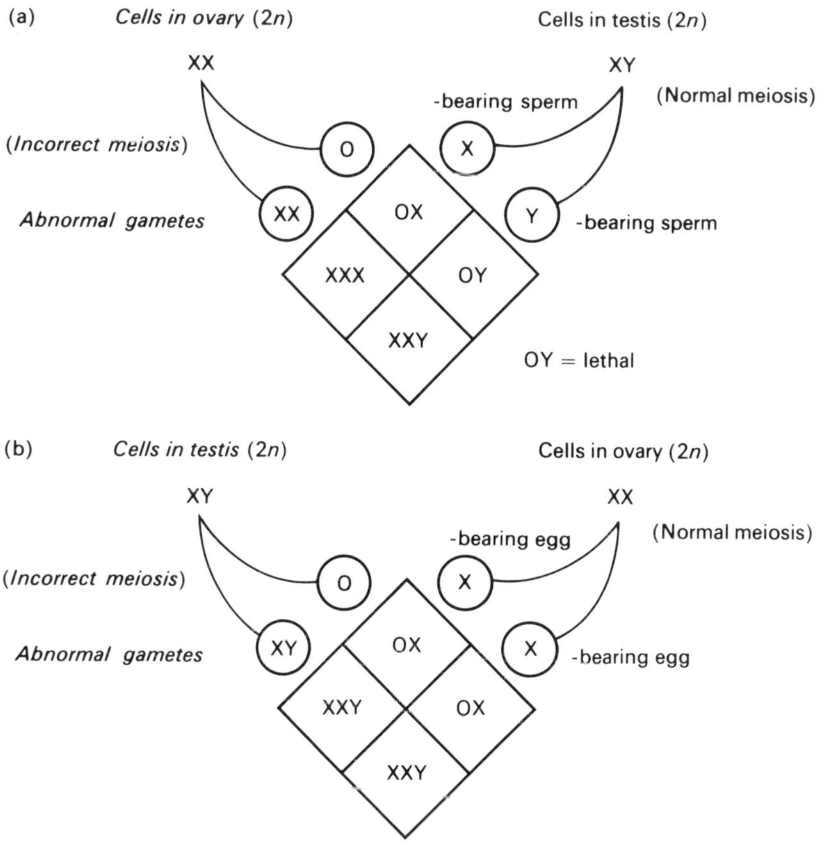
(a)
Cells in ovary (2n)
Cells in testis (2n)
XX
XY
-bearing sperm
(Normal meiosis)
(Incorrect meiosis)
O
X
Abnormal gametes
XX
OX
Y
-bearing sperm
XXX
OY
XXY
OY = lethal
(b)
Cells in testis (2n)
Cells in ovary (2n)
XY
XX
-bearing egg
(Normal meiosis)
(Incorrect meiosis)
O
X
Abnormal gametes
XY
OX
X
-bearing egg
XXY
OX
XXY

Figure 5.7 Genetic crosses involving abnormal gametes

Genotype	Phenotypic features	Frequency per 100 000 population
XXX	Normal appearance, fertile female but usually mentally retarded	121
Klinefelter's syndrome XXY	Male but with some female secondary sexual characteristics, e.g. little facial hair, breasts may develop; small testes, sterile, low intellect	19
Turner's syndrome XO	Female, short stature, lacks normal secondary sexual chracteristics	31
XYY	Male, tall, variable intelligence may show greater tendency to criminal acts or psychopathy	98

Table 5.2 Some examples of aneuploidy in man

There are other examples of aneuploidy in man, the most common one being Down's syndrome. This is due to the non-disjunction of chromosome 21, one of the small chromosomes, so that these individuals possess 47 chromosomes instead of 46. This condition where there are three, rather than a pair of chromosomes is known as *trisomy.*

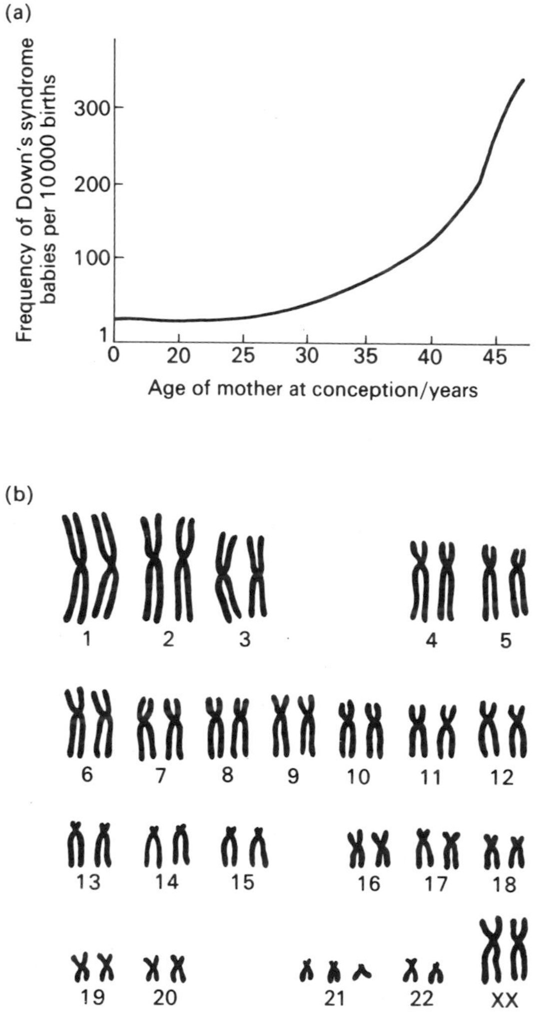
(a)
Frequency of Down's syndrome babies per 10 000 births
300
200
100
1
0
20
25
30
35
40
45
Age of mother at conception/years
(b)
1
2
3
4
5
6
7
8
9
10
11
12
13
14
15
16
17
18
19
20
21
22
XX

Figure 5.8 (a) Graph showing the incidence of Down's Syndrome births to mothers of different ages. (b) The karyotype of a Down's syndrome person

Another name for Down's syndrome, therefore, is trisomy 21. Down's individuals are often mentally retarded, have poor resistance to diseases, tend to be of stocky build and may suffer from congenital heart conditions. The risk of having a Down's syndrome child increases with the age of the mother, when meiosis seems to be rather less efficient (see Fig.5.8(a)).

Euploidy (Polyploidy)

Gamete and body cells which contain multiples of chromosome sets are called *euploids* (or polyploids). Depending on the number of multiples, three, four, etc, they are called triploid, tetraploid, etc. This condition is much more common in plants than in animals. Ferns and their relatives are often highly polyploid with hundreds of chromosomes in their body cells. This has two effects on the fern. Firstly, it slows down the process of evolution because change is only obvious when it has spread through all of the sets (as natural selection can only act on phenotypes). Secondly, it seems to confer some resistance to attack by viruses and many plants have zones of polyploid cells. Most of our important crop plants are polyploids displaying *hybrid vigour* and high yield. Polyploidy is therefore, important in evolution and artificial selection.

HYBRID VIGOUR

When two very similar varieties of organisms are bred together, they lack variation. If two dissimilar varieties are crossed, they often demonstrate much better growth, disease resistance and general hardiness. This is termed *hybrid vigour.* It arises as a result of greater genetic variety and is often made use of by plant breeders in the production of F_1 hybrids. A visit to the local garden centre will be rewarded by seeing lots of packets of seeds with the phrase 'F_1 hybrids' printed on them. However, it should be noted that if these 'vigorous hybrid plants' are allowed to flower and self-pollinate, the resulting F_2 offspring will be plants similar to the original less vigourous varieties.

MULTIPLE ALLELES

Because chromosomes occur in pairs it is only possible for two alleles of a gene to be represented, i.e. one on each chromosome. However, there are some genes which are represented by more than two alleles, i.e. multiple alleles. The simplest example to study is the gene which determines whether you are in the A, B, AB or O blood group. You will be in one of these blood groups but you may not know how you inherited your group.

There are three alleles involved in blood grouping. These alleles are denoted by the letters I^A, I^B and I^O as they are all alleles of the gene I (I represents the gene locus and stands for isoagglutinogen). The presence of the I^A allele results in a particular protein (isoagglutinogen A) being present in the cell membrane of red blood cells. The presence of the I^B allele results in a different protein (isoagglutinogen B) being present in the cell membrane. The presence of the I^o allele result in neither protein being present. The blood groups and possible genotypes found, with each of the three alleles in different combinations, are as follows:

Blood group (phenotype)	*Genotype*
A	I^AI^A or I^AI^O
B	I^BI^B or I^BI^O
AB	I^AI^B
O	I^OI^O

Q Can you work out which of the alleles is dominant, codominant and recessive from the information above? (See answer on page 98.)

Using the letters A and B to represent the protein type in the cell membrane it is possible to show these various blood groups diagramatically as shown in Fig.5.9.

Knowledge of blood groups is essential for successful blood transfusions. If the wrong type of donor blood is given to the recipient the red blood cells will clump together and death can occur. This

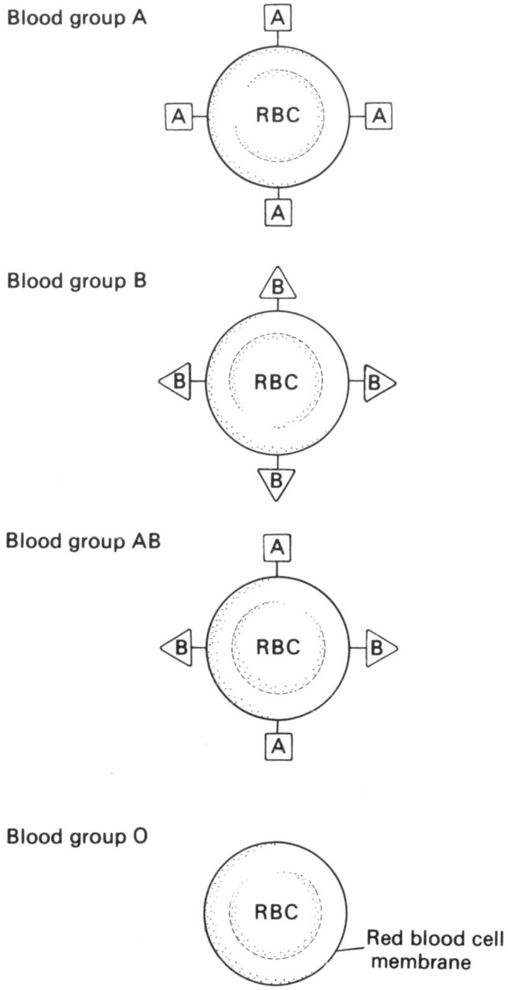
Blood group A
A
RBC
Blood group B
B
Blood group AB
Blood group O
Red blood cell membrane

Figure 5.9 Diagrammatic representation of red blood cells (RBC) from blood groups A, B, AB and O

is because there are sticky proteins called *antibodies* floating in the recipient's blood. These antibodies have a specific shape to match the protein molecules in the red blood cell membranes. The antibodies which stick to protein A are called anti-A, whilst the ones which stick to protein B are called anti-B. The diagrams shown in Fig.5.10 show how these antibodies can bind to the red blood cells and cause them to clump (or clot) together.

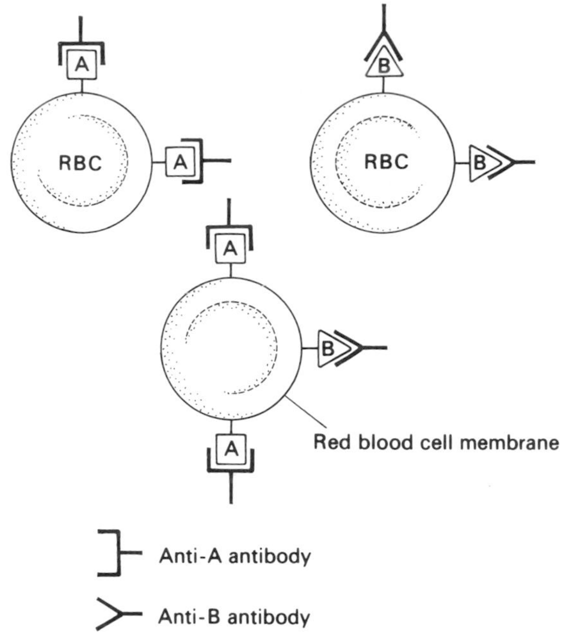
A
RBC
A
B
RBC
B
A
B
A
Red blood cell membrane
Anti-A antibody
Anti-B antibody

Figure 5.10 Binding of anti-A and anti-B antibodies to red blood cells from different blood groups

It would be 'bad design' for someone with blood group A or blood group AB to have anti-A antibodies in their blood. It would be equally 'bad design' for someone with blood group B or blood group AB to have anti-B antibodies in their blood. For this reason, people with blood group A have only anti-B antibodies in their blood and people with blood group B have only anti-A antibodies. People with blood group O have both anti-A and anti-B antibodies while people with blood group AB have neither antibody present in their blood. In this way, the possibility of red blood cells clotting does not exist under natural circumstances.

There is a real danger, however, that blood clotting could happen during a transfusion. Table 5.3 shows the possible combinations of donor and recipient blood. Some of the successful transfusions have been given a tick.

Q 1. Copy the table below and use plus and minus signs to complete it, (a plus represents a successful transfusion). As an added clue you should know that you are allowed in an emergency to clump *some* of the recipient's blood due to antibodies in the donor's blood, but you must not clump the donor's blood.

2. From the table, identify the blood group or groups of people who can donate their blood to anybody, i.e. *universal donors*, and those who can receive their blood from anybody, i.e. *universal recipients*. (See answer on page 98.)

Recipient	**Donor**			
	A (anti-B)	B (anti-A)	AB AB	O (anti-A and anti-B)
A (anti-B)	+	-		
B (anti-A)				
AB	+		+	
O (anti-A and anti-B)				

Table 5.3

■ MULTIPLE CHOICE QUESTIONS

1. A woman who is a carrier of colour blindness had phenotypically normal parents and is married to a man with normal colour vision. Which of the following statements is true?

A Her father must have been a carrier of colour blindness.
B Her mother also possessed the allele for colour blindness
C All her sons will be colour blind.
D All of her daughters will carry the recessive gene.

2. Haemophilia is a sex-linked recessive condition in man. A normal male married a woman whose father had died of haemophilia. Their children would be expected to be

A equal numbers of normal and haemophiliacs regardless of sex.
B carrier females, normal females, haemophilic males and normal males in equal numbers.
C all normal.
D normal females and haemophilic males in equal numbers.

3. Coat colour in cats is sex linked. The allele **g** produces ginger fur and the allele **b** produces black fur. Females with the genotype $\mathbf{X^gX^b}$ have tortoishell fur (a mixture of black and ginger). A ginger female and a black male produced a litter consisting of two tortoishell females, one ginger male and one tortoishell male. The genotype of the tortoishell male was

A $\mathbf{X^gX^gY}$.
B $\mathbf{X^gY}$.
C $\mathbf{X^bY}$.
D $\mathbf{X^bX^bY}$.
E $\mathbf{X^bX^gY}$.

4. The most likely cause of the genotype produced in Multiple Choice Question 3 was

A non-disjunction of the sex chromosomes in the female.
B non-disjunction of the sex chromosomes in the male.
C a translocation of the sex chromosomes in the female.
D a mutation of the X chromosome in the male.

5. Colour blindness is a sex-linked trait. The allele for colour blindness is recessive to the normal condition. A man with normal vision and a woman who was colour blind had a child with normal vision and a sex chromosome arrangement of XXY. This suggests non-disjunction during the production of the

A sperm and eggs.
B sperm only.
C eggs only.
D sperm or egg.

(See answers on page 98.)

END OF CHAPTER QUESTIONS

Having read, and hopefully understood, the preceding chapters you should now be able to attempt some genetics problems on codominance, mutations and multiple alleles.

1. *A 'fowl' problem*

Blue Andalusian chickens are produced by crossing pure-breeding splashed white with pure-breeding black parents. The splashed white parents lack the allele for the formation of melanin whilst the black parents produce large amounts of this pigment. The F_1 crosses show a partial development of melanin resulting in the blue condition.

(a) Using the symbol **M** for the allele for melanin production and the symbol **m** for the absence of melanin production, show why a cross between black and splashed white individuals produces blue offspring.
(b) Using the same symbols, show the expected offspring if the blue F_1 chickens were then interbred.
(c) What would be the expected offspring from the following two crosses?
(i) blue Andalusian x splashed white;
(ii) blue Andalusian x black.
(See answers on page 99.)

2. *Pink antirrhinums*

A packet of antirrhinum (snapdragon) seeds was sown and a wonderful show of pink-flowered plants were produced. They were so good that the gardener decided to save some of the seeds produced by the pink plants. The following season however was rather disappointing because only half of the plants were pink-flowered. The remainder of the plants were either white-flowered or red-flowered (in roughly equal proportions).

(a) Explain why these results were obtained.
(b) Suggest what could be done to obtain all pink-flowered plants in the following season.
(c) What would you do to obtain (i) pure red or (ii) pure white plants the following year?
(See answers on page 100.)

3. *Disputed paternity*

A colourblind farmer whose blood group was **AB** married a woman with normal vision whose blood group was **O**. The farmer's wife had three children Harry, Barry and Carrie. Barry and Carrie were both lazy, dull individuals who did little to help on the farm. Harry, however, was a tall, good-looking, intelligent and hard-working young man. The farmer grew impatient with his wife who also seldom helped on the farm. He decided that he could not possibly be the father of three such different children and challenged his wife suspecting that she had been unfaithful.

(a) Consider the facts below:
Harry – blood group **O** normal vision
Barry – blood group **A** normal vision
Carrie – blood group **B** colourblind
What does this tell you about the family?
(b) What further information can you give about the genotype of the farmer's wife? Explain your answer.
(See answers on page 101.)

4. *More about cats*

The genes controlling coat colour in cats are situated on the **X** chromosomes and are codominant. A ginger–coated female is crossed with a black male. All of the male offspring are ginger and all of the female offspring are tortoiseshell (a mixture of black and ginger fur).

(a) Show, by means of suitable genetic diagrams, why this is so.
(b) What would be the offspring of the following three crosses?
(i) black female x ginger male:
(ii) tortoiseshell female x ginger male;
(iii) tortoiseshell female x black male.
(c) Occasionally, a tortoiseshell male is produced. These males are always sterile. Show, by means of a genetic diagram how this result is possible.
(See answers on page 102.)

CHAPTER 6

MORE OF MENDEL AND MATHEMATICS!

DIHYBRID INHERITANCE

The pioneering work of Gregor Mendel did not end with his study of the inheritance of individual characteristics in pea plants. He conducted more complex breeding experiments in which he looked at the way in which more than one characteristic was inherited. He was curious to find out whether features such as seed shape (round seeds and wrinkled seeds) was inherited alongside such features as plant height (tall plants and short plants). Indeed this work, investigating combinations of characters, is the very stuff of modern breeding programmes where several desirable characteristics are required in one plant. Investigating the inheritance of just one characteristic is called *monohybrid inheritance*. Investigating two characteristics is called *dihybid inheritance.*

Mendel carried out several different crosses and concluded that many characteristics *assorted independently* when compared together. The principle of independent assortment applies to genes which are located on different chromosomes.

Mendel crossed pure breeding pea plants which had yellow, round seeds with pea plants which had green, wrinkled seeds. The first generation of plants produced seeds which were all yellow and round. This confirmed that 'yellow' and 'round' are the two dominant alleles.

He then went on to self-pollinate the F_1 plants. If you are reasonably good at genetics, you will realise that the F_2 offspring should contain plants which produce round to wrinkled seeds in the ratio of 3:1, and yellow to green seeds in a similar ratio of 3:1. But what would be the proportion of yellow and round, yellow and wrinkled, green and round and green and wrinkled seeds in the F_2 plants?

The F_2 plants, in fact, produced all four combinations of seed colour and shape (see Fig. 6.1).

Repeated experiments produced ratios close to those listed here:

yellow, round	9/16 (actual number 315)
yellow, wrinkled	3/16 (actual number 101)
green, round	3/16 (actual number 108)
green, wrinkled	1/16 (actual number 32)

Mendel used his particulate theory to explain the results. The characteristics did not blend together, it was as if they were passed on as discrete units at random. (Refer back to Fig.2.7 to check how this happens at gamete formation during meiosis.) Since there are two pairs of alleles involved, the F_1 plants can produce four types of gamete in equal proportions. Fertilisation is a random process so there is a one in four chance of selecting a particular combination of the two alleles in a pollen grain and a one in four chance of it fusing with a similar combination of alleles in an ovule.

Mendel noted that the 9:3:3:1 ratio was obtained when a dihybrid cross was carried out using pure–breeding parents and self-pollinating the resultant F_1 offspring. He had already developed a way of finding whether an organism was pure breeding by carrying out a *test cross* (see page 40).

In a monohybrid test cross, the organism to be investigated is crossed with a homozygous recessive. If the resulting offspring are all alike, the parent being tested must be homozygous. However, if the parent being tested is heterozygous, the resulting offspring will segregate into two types in roughly equal numbers. For example, a variety of pea with round seeds (round is dominant) is tested using a wrinkled-seeded variety. The wrinkled-seeded variety must be homozygous since wrinkled seeds are recessive. The test cross is summarised in Fig.6.2.

Thus in Fig.6.2(a) the round–seeded plant must be homozygous whereas in Fig.6.2(b) the round–seeded plant must be heterozygous.

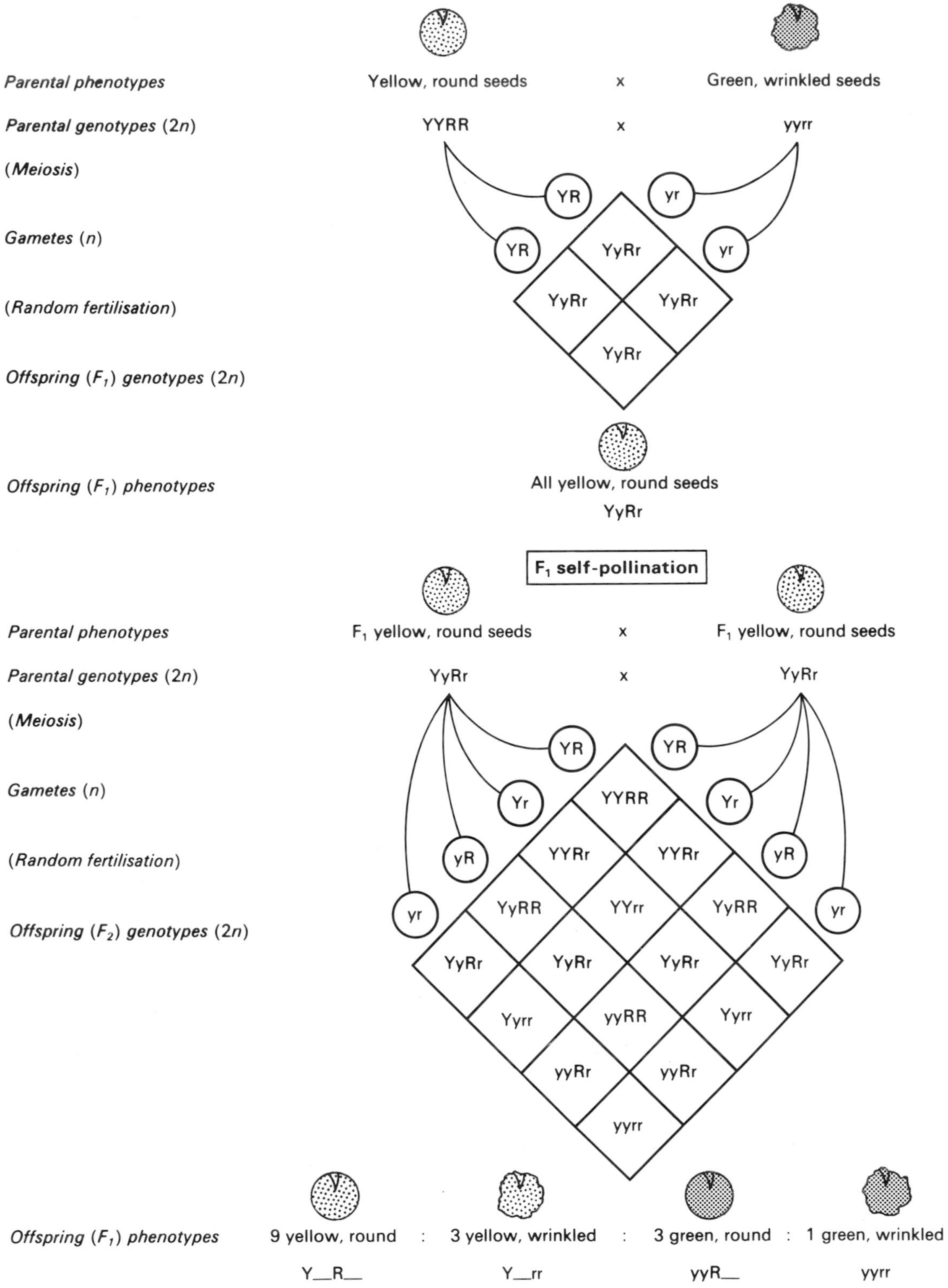
Parental phenotypes
Yellow, round seeds
x
Green, wrinkled seeds
Parental genotypes (2n)
YYRR
x
yyrr
(Meiosis)
Gametes (n)
YR
YR
yr
yr
(Random fertilisation)
YyRr
YyRr
YyRr
YyRr
Offspring (F1) genotypes (2n)
Offspring (F1) phenotypes
All yellow, round seeds
YyRr
F1 self-pollination
Parental phenotypes
F1 yellow, round seeds
x
F1 yellow, round seeds
Parental genotypes (2n)
YyRr
x
YyRr
(Meiosis)
Gametes (n)
YR
Yr
yR
yr
YR
Yr
yR
yr
(Random fertilisation)
Offspring (F2) genotypes (2n)
YYRR
YYRr
YYRr
YyRR
YYrr
YyRR
YyRr
YyRr
YyRr
YyRr
Yyrr
yyRR
Yyrr
yyRr
yyRr
yyrr
Offspring (F1) phenotypes
9 yellow, round
:
3 yellow, wrinkled
:
3 green, round
:
1 green, wrinkled
Y__R__
Y__rr
yyR__
yyrr

Figure 6.1 An explanation of Mendel's dihybrid crosses

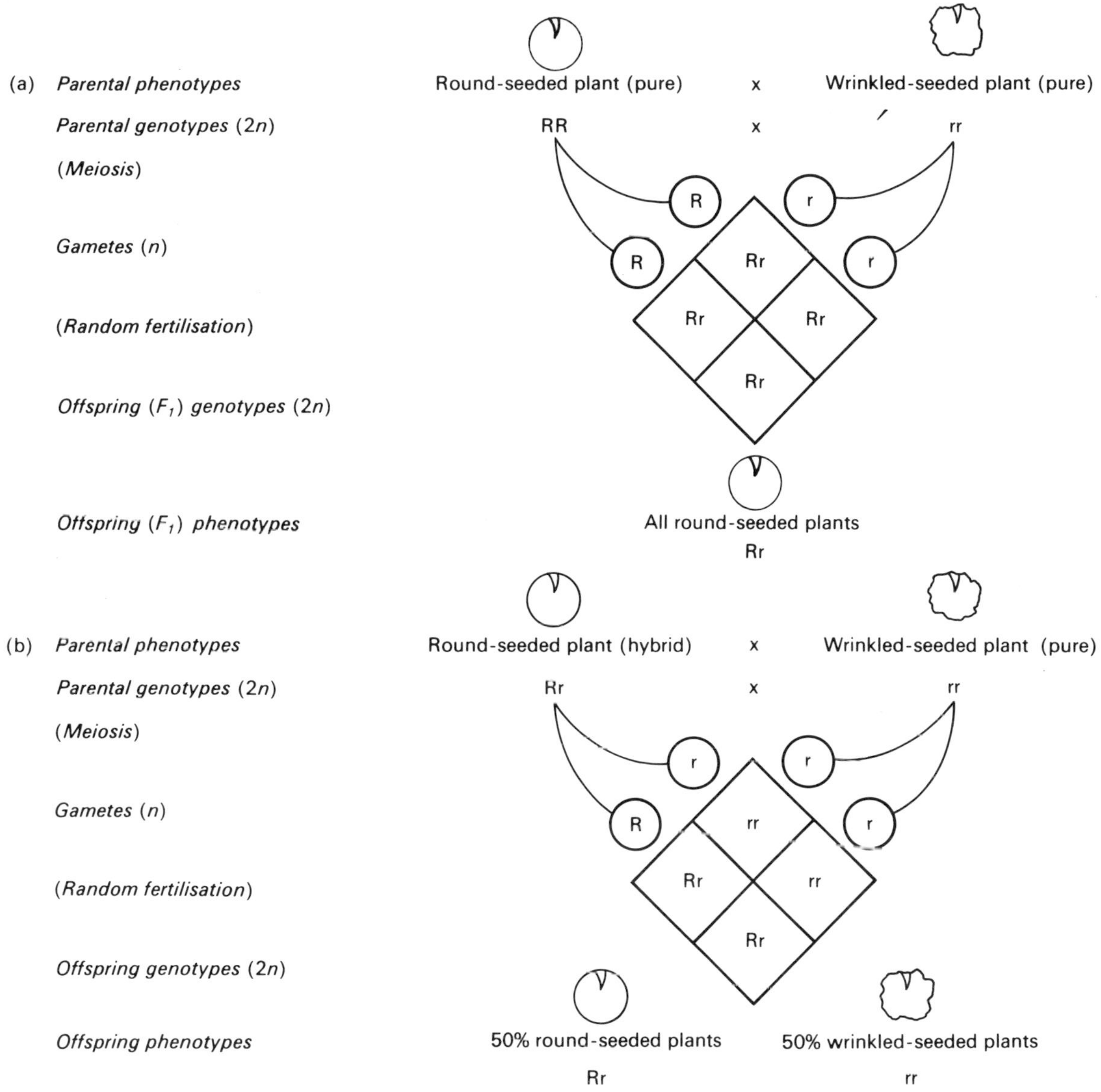

(a) Parental phenotypes
Round-seeded plant (pure)
x
Wrinkled-seeded plant (pure)
Parental genotypes (2n)
RR
x
rr
(Meiosis)
Gametes (n)
R
R
r
r
(Random fertilisation)
Rr
Rr
Rr
Rr
Offspring (F_1) genotypes (2n)
Offspring (F_1) phenotypes
All round-seeded plants
Rr
(b) Parental phenotypes
Round-seeded plant (hybrid)
x
Wrinkled-seeded plant (pure)
Parental genotypes (2n)
Rr
x
rr
(Meiosis)
Gametes (n)
r
R
r
r
(Random fertilisation)
rr
Rr
rr
Rr
Offspring genotypes (2n)
Offspring phenotypes
50% round-seeded plants
Rr
50% wrinkled-seeded plants
rr

Figure 6.2 Test crosses to identify homozygous and heterozygous plants

Mendel then went on to do similar kinds of test crosses with the dihybrid plants. If the heterozygous F_1 plants, produced by crossing pure breeding green and wrinkled-seeded plants with pure breeding yellow and round-seeded plants, were tested by breeding them with green and wrinkled-seeded plants, they produced a 1:1:1:1 ratio (see Fig.6.3).

MENDEL'S LAWS OF GENETICS

Mendel formulated several Laws of Genetics. Two of them concern you as a student at this level.

Mendel's First Law

This Law is sometimes called the *Principle of Segregation*. This Law is basic to an understanding of genetics and states that in an organism which is heterozygous for a particular condition, the gametes of that organism will contain either allele in a ratio of 1:1. If a heterozygous tall pea plant is used to illustrate this Law, then the pollen grains and ovules of that plant should contain either **T** or **t** in the ratio of 1:1. Usually this Law is illustrated by the 3:1 ratio obtained when a heterozygous organism is self-pollinated (i.e. crossed with another heterozygote), or when it is crossed with a homozygous recessive to produce a 1:1 ratio.

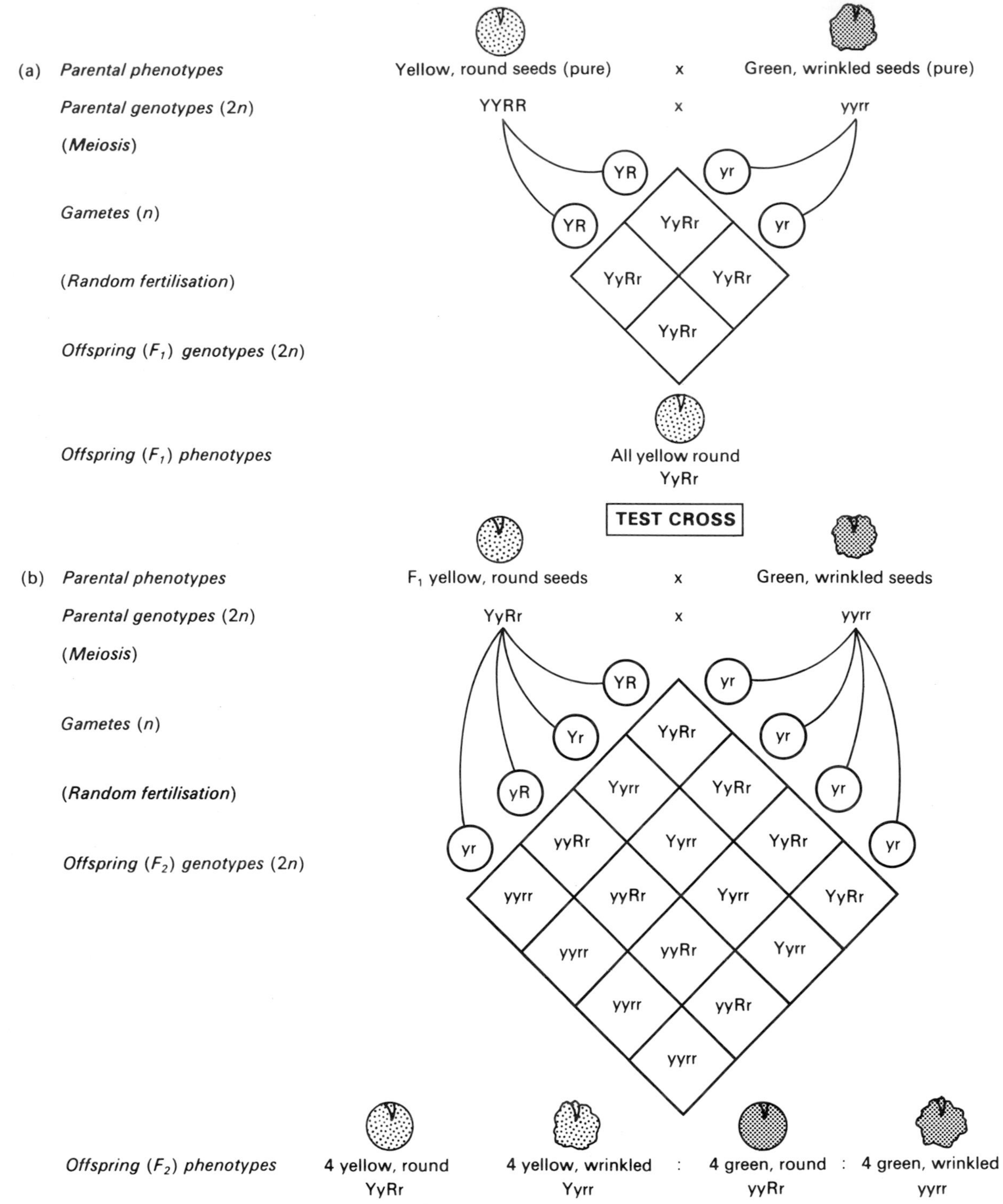
(a) Parental phenotypes
Yellow, round seeds (pure) x Green, wrinkled seeds (pure)
Parental genotypes (2n)
YYRR x yyrr
(Meiosis)
Gametes (n)
YR YR yr yr
(Random fertilisation)
YyRr YyRr YyRr YyRr
Offspring (F_1) genotypes (2n)
Offspring (F_1) phenotypes
All yellow round
YyRr
TEST CROSS
(b) Parental phenotypes
F_1 yellow, round seeds x Green, wrinkled seeds
Parental genotypes (2n)
YyRr x yyrr
(Meiosis)
Gametes (n)
YR Yr yR yr yr yr yr yr
(Random fertilisation)
Offspring (F_2) genotypes (2n)
YyRr Yyrr YyRr yyRr Yyrr YyRr yyrr yyRr Yyrr YyRr yyrr yyRr Yyrr yyrr yyRr yyrr
Offspring (F_2) phenotypes
4 yellow, round YyRr
4 yellow, wrinkled Yyrr
:
4 green, round yyRr
:
4 green, wrinkled yyrr

Figure 6.3 Mendel's test cross using dihybrid plants

Mendel's Second Law

This Law is sometimes called the *Principle of Independent Assortment*. This Law states that genes assort themselves at random and that the inheritance of one characteristic is independent of the inheritance of another characteristic. This is true unless the genes are linked (i.e. both are on the same chromosome see page 66). Usually this Law is illustrated by the 9:3:3:1 ratio obtained when organisms which are heterozygous for both characteristics are self-fertilised.

FURTHER QUESTIONS

Here are three questions which will test your understanding of the dihybrid ratio. After you have attempted an answer, check your workings with the answers at the back of the book.

1. A pure breeding grey-bodied, vestigial-winged fruit fly was crossed with a pure breeding ebony-bodied, normal-winged fruit fly. All the F_1 fruit flies were grey-bodied and normal-winged.

(a) Draw a diagram to illustrate this genetic cross.
(b) Which are the dominent alleles in this cross?
The F_1 fruit flies produced in the above cross were then allowed to interbreed. A representative sample of the F_2 flies is shown below.

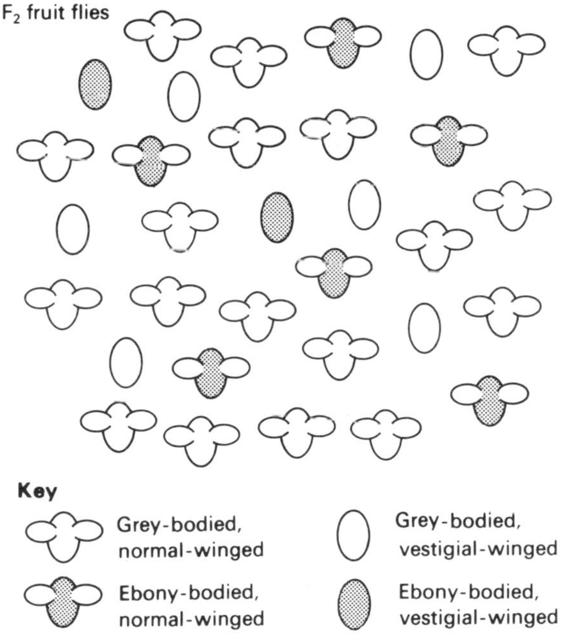
F2 fruit flies
Key
Grey-bodied, normal-winged
Grey-bodied, vestigial-winged
Ebony-bodied, normal-winged
Ebony-bodied, vestigial-winged

(c) Use the key to identify and count for the four types of F_2 offspring produced.
(d) Draw a diagram to illustrate the genetic cross between two F_1 fruit flies.
(e) What evidence is there that body colour and wing shape in fruit flies are inherited independently of each other?
(See answers on page 103.)

2. In guinea pigs, short fur is dominant to long fur and black coat is dominant to white. A cross was made between a pure breeding long-haired, black guinea pig and a pure breeding short-haired, white guinea pig.
a) What would be the expected coat colour and length of fur of the offspring from this cross?
b) Suppose that the offspring were allowed to breed together. What would be the expected genotypes and phenotypes of the resulting F_2 generation?
c) One of the F_2 guinea pigs had short black fur. When mated with a white guinea pig with long fur, all of the offspring had short fur, but the ratio of black guinea pigs to white ones was 50:50. Explain how these results could be obtained.
(See answers on page 104.)

3. In a certain plant, the flower petals are normally purple. Two recessive mutations have occurred in separate plants and have been found to be on different chromosomes.
Mutation 1 (**m_1**) gives blue petals when homozygous (i.e. **m_1m_1**).
Mutation 2 (**m_2**) gives red petals when homozygous (i.e. **m_2m_2**).
Biochemists working on the synthesis of flower pigments in this species have already described the following pathway:

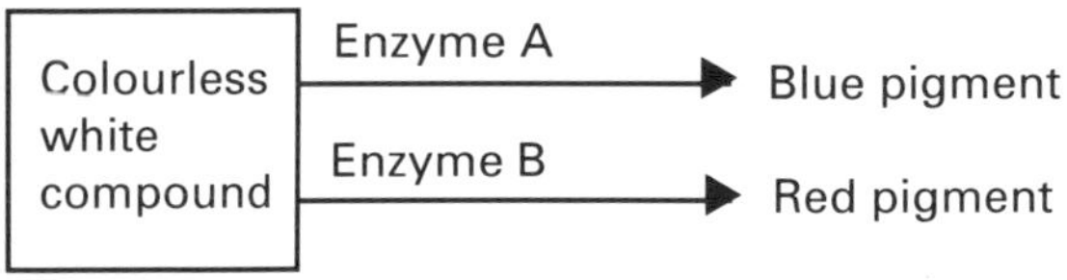
Colourless white compound
Enzyme A
Blue pigment
Enzyme B
Red pigment

(a) Which homozygous mutant must be deficient in enzyme A activity?
(b) A plant has a genotype **$M_1m_1M_2m_2$**
(i) What would its phenotype be?
(ii) If the plant is self-pollinated, show, by means of a full genetic explanation, what colours of progeny are expected, and in what proportions?
(c) Why are these mutations recessive?
(See answers on page 105.)

MENDEL: THE LUCKY MONK

Mendel was fortunate* in choosing characteristics such as roundness and colour of pea seeds for his breeding experiments. These two features are determined by two pairs of alleles which demonstrate simple dominance and which are located on different chromosomes. The analysis of the results was really quite straightforward and the complications caused by other effects such as codominance and linkage were avoided.

A dihybrid inheritance involving codominance

Let us consider how Mendel's 9:3:3:1 ratio might be modified if just one of the pairs of alleles involved showed codominance. Suppose for example, that a pure tall, red–flowered plant was crossed with a pure short, white–flowered plant. Assuming that tall is dominant to short and that red and white are codominant (producing pink) the F_1 plants would all be tall and have pink flowers.

The F_1 plants are then left to self-pollinate and the seeds are collected and grown to produce the F_2 generation of plants. Clearly there will be six phenotypes instead of four, i.e. tall reds, tall pinks, tall whites, short reds, short pinks and short whites. The ratio cannot be the usual 9:3:3:1 – it is said to be modified. The phenotypic ratios of such a cross are shown below. Try to work them out.

Phenotype	*Ratio*
Tall red	3/16
Tall pink	6/16
Tall white	3/16
Short red	1/16
Short pink	2/16
Short white	1/6

Note that the overall ratio of tall to short is 3:1 and that the overall ratio of red to pink to white is 1:2:1, precisely the ratios you would expect in two monohybrid crosses.

Allelomorphic genes

In Sweet peas, the flower colour is determined by two pairs of alleles. This is sometimes referred to as allelomorphism. These alleles can be represented by the letters **R** and **B**. When at least one of each allele is present in its dominant form the petals of the sweet pea are purple, otherwise they are white. This is summarised in Table 6.1.

*Fortune favours the prepared mind – Sir Alexander Fleming

Genotype	Phenotype (flower colour)
R — B —	Purple
rr— —	White
— — bb	White

Table 6.1

If a cross is made between two heterozygous purple–flowered sweet peas (**RrBb**) another modified 9:3:3:1 ratio is obtained. This time it is a 9:7 ratio of purple to white. Since this is very close to a 1:1 ratio, the two crosses can often be confused. The important thing to remember is that the 1:1 ratio comes from a test cross (with just one pair of alleles) whereas this 9:7 ratio arises from a self-cross (with two pairs of allelomorphic genes involved). You can test your understanding of this by tackling the question about red and white flowers on page 65.

Gene complexes

In the domestic chicken, the shape of the comb is affected by the interaction of genes located at two different sites on different chromosomes. The presence of a pea comb or a rose comb depends on the presence of the dominant alleles **P** and **R** respectively (see Table 6.2). When both of these alleles are present in their dominant form, the comb is described as walnut. If both alleles are present only in their recessive form, a single comb results. These four combs are shown on page 65.

Genotype	Phenotype (comb shape)
R — pp	Rose
rrP —	Pea
R — P —	Walnut
rrpp	Single

Table 6.2

A cross between a pure breeding rose comb and a pure breeding pea comb always results in a walnut comb being produced. You might like to work out what would happen if one of these walnut-combed F_1 offspring was crossed with a single-combed chicken. You should arrive at a 1:1:1:1 ratio of pea:rose:walnut:single.

Rose comb

Pea comb

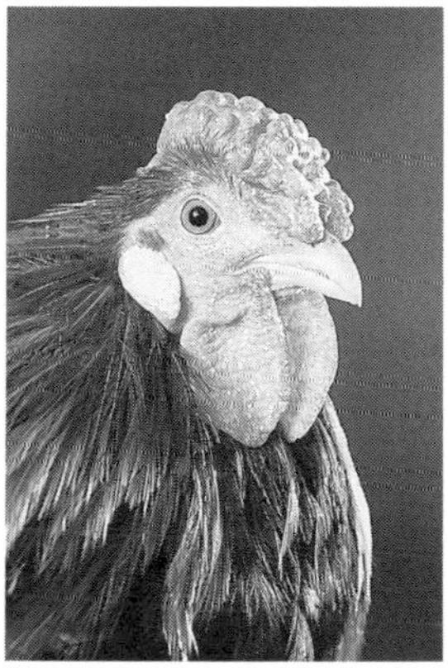

Walnut comb

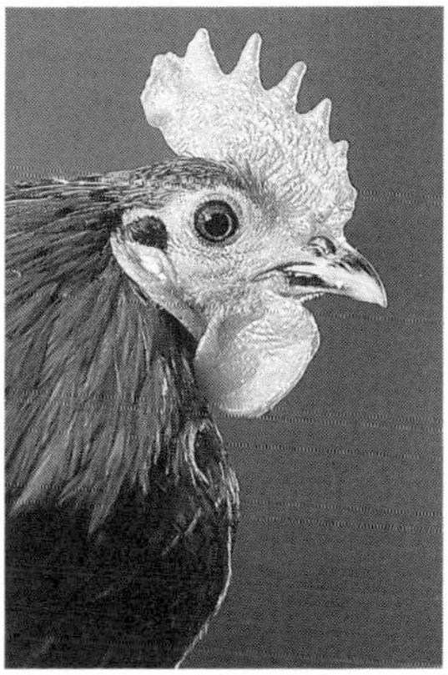

Single comb

The case of the red and white flowers

If genes are responsible for making enzymes which operate *in a sequence*, the ratios obtained in crossing experiments may differ from the usual 9:3:3:1.

Let us take an example in which a colourless substance is turned into the precursor of a pigment by an enzyme E1. This pigment precursor is then turned into a red pigment by an enzyme E2. If you remember that enzymes are coded for by genes, you might suppose that gene **A** codes for the formation of enzyme E1 and that gene **B** codes for the formation of enzyme E2.

For a red pigment to be made, both E1 and E2 must be present and so dominant alleles **A** and **B** must both be present. Suppose a plant could not make either enzyme E1 or E2, this would indicate that **A** and **B** were not working and you might assume the presence of the recessive alleles **a** and **b** (each homozygous) .

However, if a plant lacks gene **A**, it will be unable to make the red pigment since there is no precursor for enzyme E2 to act upon. This is known as *epistasis*, i.e. it is where one gene is able to affect the expression of another gene (see Fig.6.4).

Q Draw out a cross to show the expected ratio of the offspring produced when a red-flowered plant with the genotype **AaBb** is crossed with another red-flowered plant with the same genotype.

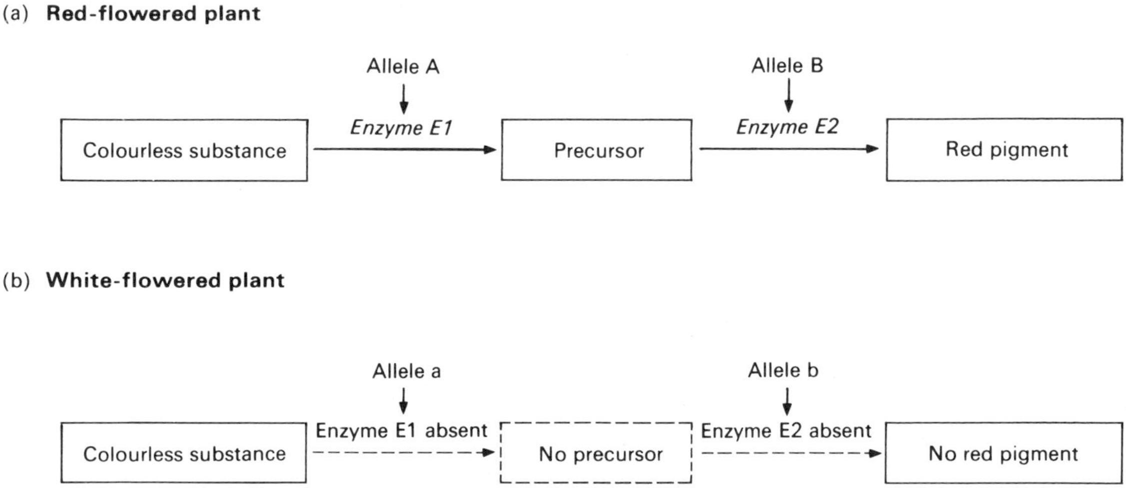
(a) Red-flowered plant
Allele A
Enzyme E1
Allele B
Enzyme E2
Colourless substance
Precursor
Red pigment
(b) White-flowered plant
Allele a
Enzyme E1 absent
Allele b
Enzyme E2 absent
Colourless substance
No precursor
No red pigment

Figure 6.4 The effects of gene expression on pigment production

LINKAGE

We have discussed dihybrid inheritance and independent assortment where the genes are on different chromosomes. This, however, is not the only situation possible: a greater range of gametes can be made.

To help understand this idea it is best to start by looking at a situation where the genotype of each characteristic is heterozygous e.g. **AaBb**. The alleles for each gene can either be found on the same pair of homologous chromosomes or on a different pair as shown in Fig.6.5(a) and (b).

When the two genes or their alleles are found on the same pair of homologous chromosomes they are said to be *linked* or to show *linkage*. When the two genes or their alleles are found on different pairs of homologous chromosomes they are said to show *independent assortment*. Whether or not the genes are linked is important when it comes to producing gametes. If you understand meiosis (see page 28) you will understand how differences can occur in the types of gamete which can be made.

If the genes are linked, only two types of gamete are possible. Separation of the homologous chromosomes in the first stage of meiosis ensures that this will happen. In Fig.6.5(c) the dominant allele of both genes is found on the same chromosome of the homologous pair. This situation is known as *coupling*. The dominant alleles could also be found on different chromosomes of the homologous pair, a situation known as *repulsion* (see Fig. 6.5(d)). However, only one of these situations can exist and, whichever it is, only two types of gamete are possible.

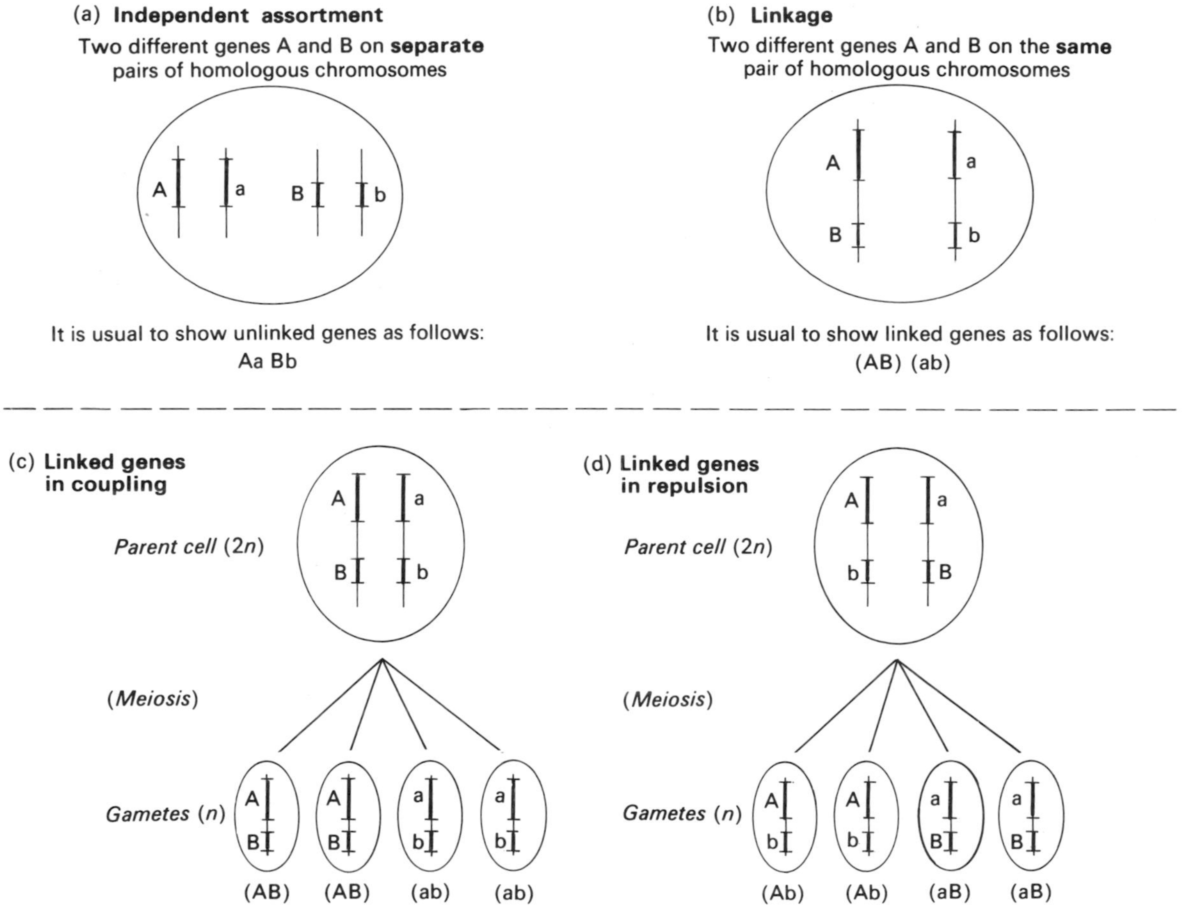
(a) Independent assortment
Two different genes A and B on separate pairs of homologous chromosomes
A a B b
It is usual to show unlinked genes as follows:
Aa Bb
(b) Linkage
Two different genes A and B on the same pair of homologous chromosomes
A a B b
It is usual to show linked genes as follows:
(AB) (ab)
(c) Linked genes in coupling
Parent cell (2n)
A a B b
(Meiosis)
Gametes (n)
(AB) (AB) (ab) (ab)
(d) Linked genes in repulsion
Parent cell (2n)
A a b B
(Meiosis)
Gametes (n)
(Ab) (Ab) (aB) (aB)

Figure 6.5 Possible arrangements of a pair of genes. Note that linked genes can be arranged in one of two ways in a heterozygous individual. If the two dominant alleles are on the same chromosome, they are said to be in coupling (see diagram (c)). If they are on different chromosomes, they are said to be in repulsion (see diagram (d))

There are four types of gamete that can be made if the alleles are found on different pairs of homologous chromosome. Once again, this is due to the way the chromosomes move about during meiosis. The crucial point to appreciate is the way they line up in pairs at the equator in the metaphase of the first stage. Cell P and Cell Q in Fig.6.6 show two different ways in which the pairs could line up.

There is an equal chance of either of these ways happening in each of the many cells which are used to make gametes e.g. the cells in the seminiferous tubules of the male testis involved in making sperm. This is illustrated in Fig.6.7.

There is no rule which says that all the dominant alleles must line up on the left-hand side during meiotic cell division of the gamete-making cells. The way in which one pair of chromosomes align themselves has no influence on the way in which another pair align themselves. The pairs of chromosomes are said to arrange or assort themselves independently on the equator of the cell – hence the term *independent assortment*.

When the pairs of chromosomes are pulled apart during the first stage of meiosis, it is inevitable that the second stage will result in four types of gamete being made. Two types will be made by those cells in which the chromosomes line up with the dominant alleles on the same side (i.e. **AB** and **ab**) and the other two types will be made by those cells in which the chromosome with the dominant allele of one gene lines up on the same side of the equator with the chromosome carrying the recessive allele of the other gene (i.e. **Ab** and **aB**). Therefore, four types of gamete are produced altogether.

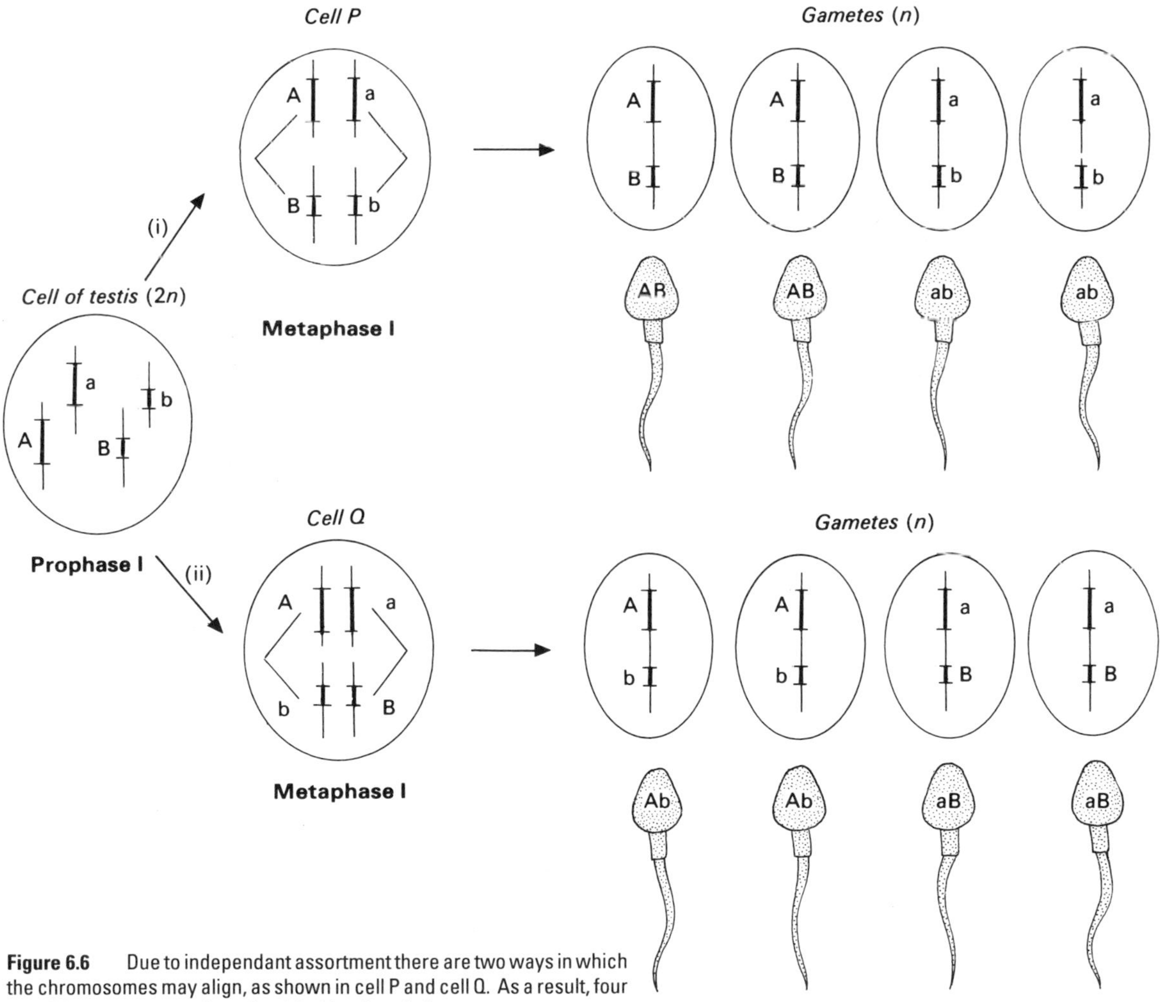
Cell P
Gametes (n)
A
a
B
b
A
B
A
B
a
b
a
b
AB
AB
ab
ab
(i)
Cell of testis (2n)
Metaphase I
a
b
A
B
Prophase I
(ii)
Cell Q
Gametes (n)
A
a
b
B
A
b
A
b
a
B
a
B
Metaphase I
Ab
Ab
aB
aB

Figure 6.6 Due to independant assortment there are two ways in which the chromosomes may align, as shown in cell P and cell Q. As a result, four possible gametes may form, i.e. AB, Ab, aB and ab

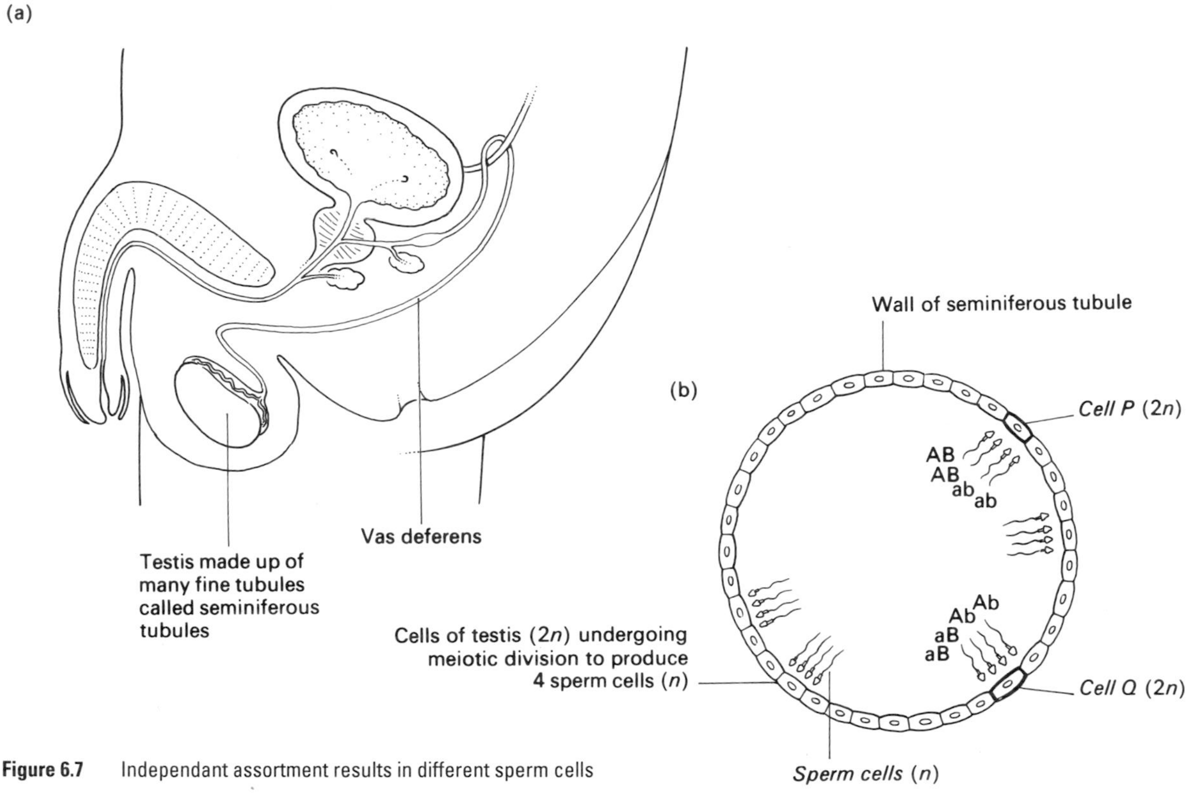
(a)
Testis made up of many fine tubules called seminiferous tubules
Vas deferens
Cells of testis (2n) undergoing meiotic division to produce 4 sperm cells (n)
(b)
Wall of seminiferous tubule
Cell P (2n)
AB
AB
ab
ab
Ab
Ab
aB
aB
Cell Q (2n)
Sperm cells (n)

Figure 6.7 Independant assortment results in different sperm cells

More About Linkage: Crossing Over

We have just stated that only two types of gamete can be made if the genes are linked. As with most statements there are often exceptions, and if a process called *crossing over* occurs two new types of gamete can also be made, making four in all.

Crossing over occurs when pieces of one chromosome are swapped with pieces of another chromosome during a very early stage in meiosis. The genes on the pieces of chromosome are also swapped in the process. Fig.6.8 illustrates this process and also shows the types of gamete that can be made.

Most of the cells which make gametes will not undergo crossing over and the gametes they produce are called *parental types*. The new gene combinations produced in the gametes made by the few cells in which crossing over has occurred represent what are called the non-parental or *recombinant types*.

Table 6.3 shows the different types of gamete that can be made by a heterozygous parent (AaBb) under varying circumstances.

Circumstance	Gamete genotype
Independent assortment	AB Ab aB ab in equal proportions
Linkage (coupling)	AB ab in equal proportions
Linkage (repulsion)	Ab aB in equal proportions
Linkage (coupling and crossing over)	Most AB and ab, fewer Ab and aB
Linkage (repulsion and crossing over)	Most Ab and aB, fewer AB and ab

Table 6.3

At fertilisation, random joining of gametes occurs resulting in a much wider diversity of offspring. If each parent can produce four different types of gamete, then there are sixteen possible combinations of genetic material.

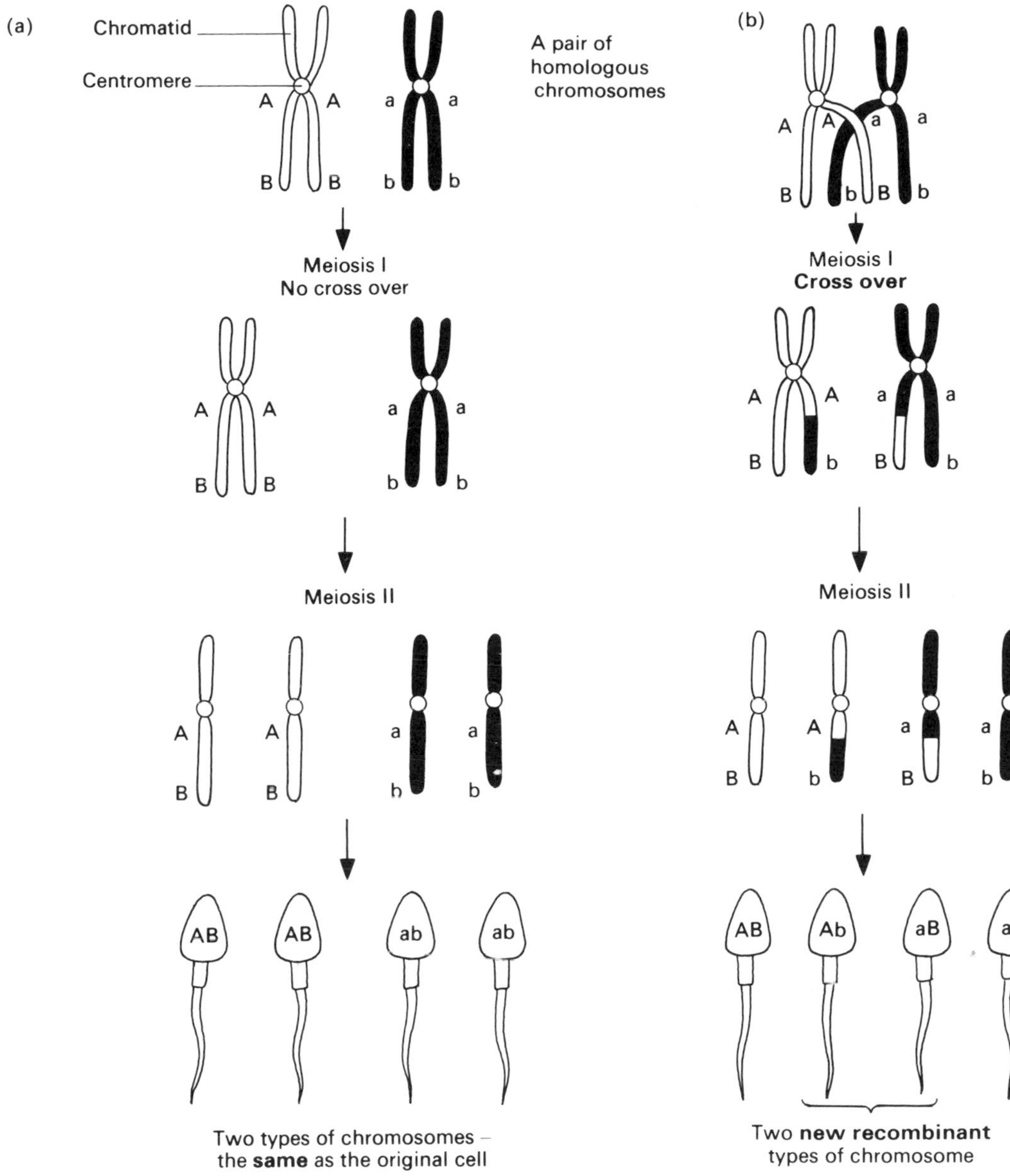
(a)
Chromatid
Centromere
A pair of homologous chromosomes
A A a a
B B b b
Meiosis I
No cross over
Meiosis II
AB AB ab ab
Two types of chromosomes – the **same** as the original cell
(b)
Meiosis I
Cross over
Meiosis II
AB Ab aB ab
Two **new recombinant** types of chromosome

Figure 6.8 Linkage and crossing over results in the formation of novel combinations of alleles. The frequency of crossing over can be used to map the position of genes on a chromosome

■ SOLVING PROBLEMS OF LINKAGE AND CROSSING OVER

Earlier examples involved crosses where the genes were located on different chromosomes, i.e. they were not linked. When the genes are linked on the same chromosome, the pattern of inheritance is different. When one allele is present in a gamete, the linked allele is usually present too. In some cases however, and this is usually less frequent, new combinations of alleles can arise. This must be because the chromatids carrying the two alleles have crossed over and exchanged information during prophase 1 of meiosis. Look back to the diagram (Fig.2.7 page 28) to remind yourself of this phase.

How linkage affects the outcome of a cross

In mice, the gene for tail length is located on the same chromosome as the gene for type of coat.

Short tail **S** is dominant to normal tail **s** and normal coat **W** is dominant to wavy coat **w**. If a cross is made between a pure breeding short-tailed mouse with a normal coat, i.e. (**SW**) (**SW**) and a pure breeding normal-tailed mouse with a wavy coat, i.e. (**sw**) (**sw**), all of the offspring have short tails and normal coats (see Fig.6.9(a)). Brackets are used to show that two alleles are linked on the same chromosome, e.g. (**sw**) and (**SW**).

The offspring have the genetic make up (**SW**) (**sw**). They are then crossed with pure breeding normal-tailed mice with a wavy coat. Instead of producing just two types of offspring, four different types are produced. Table 6.4 shows the results of several of these crosses.

The genetic diagrams in Fig.6.9(b) and (c) show how the four different types of mice are produced.

Appearance of mice in the F_2 generation	**Number**
Short-tailed, normal coat	91
Short-tailed, wavy coat	8
Long-tailed, normal coat	9
Long-tailed, wavy coat	92

Table 6.4

The mice with short tails and wavy coats, and the mice with long tails and normal coats were produced as a result of crossing over. The closer together the gene loci are situated, the less frequently crossing over occurs. In this case 17 mice from a total of 200 were a result of crossing over, a frequency of 8.5%. Using the results of many crosses such as this, it is possible to map chromosomes and locate the relative positions of a large number of different genes.

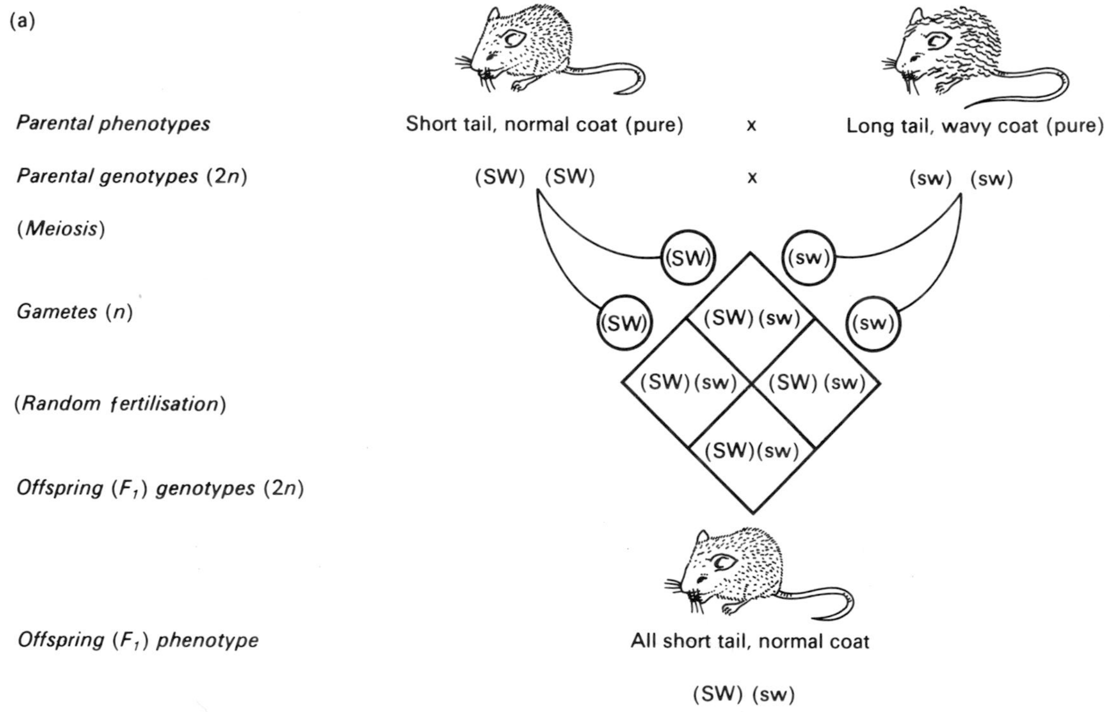
(a)
Parental phenotypes
Short tail, normal coat (pure)
x
Long tail, wavy coat (pure)
Parental genotypes (2n)
(SW) (SW)
x
(sw) (sw)
(Meiosis)
Gametes (n)
(SW)
(SW)
(sw)
(sw)
(Random fertilisation)
(SW) (sw)
(SW) (sw)
(SW) (sw)
(SW)(sw)
Offspring (F_1) genotypes (2n)
Offspring (F_1) phenotype
All short tail, normal coat
(SW) (sw)

Figure 6.9(a)

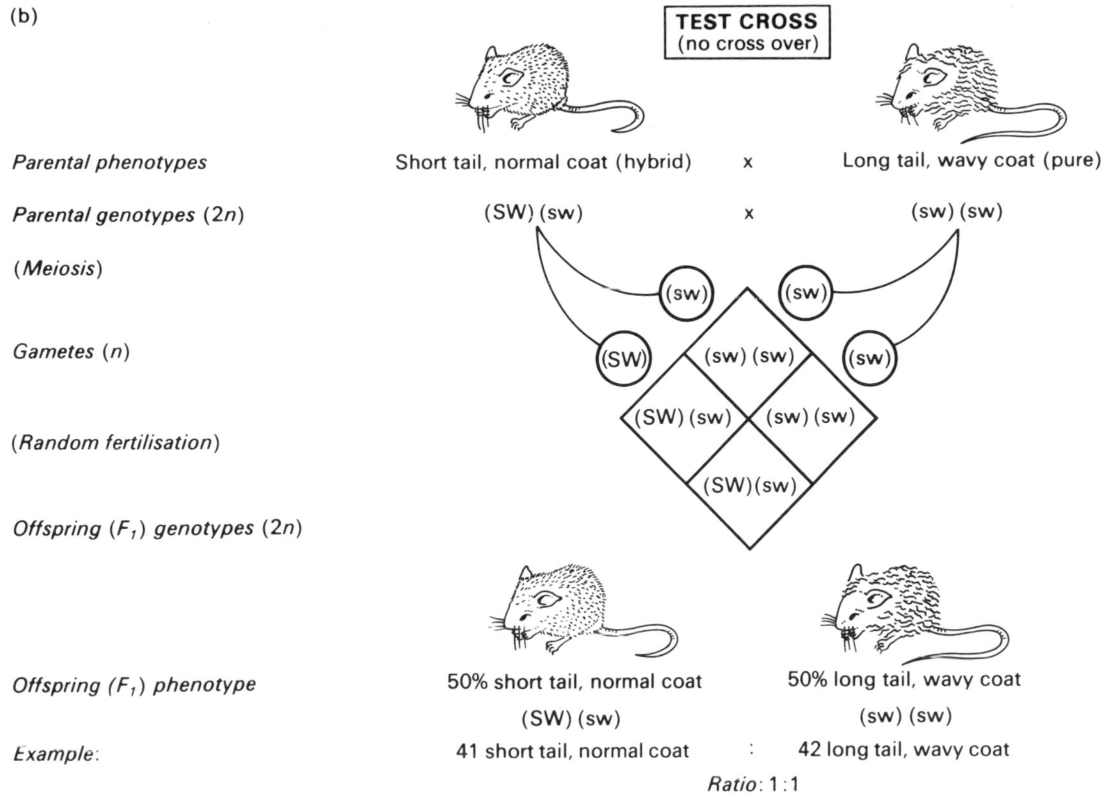
(b)
TEST CROSS
(no cross over)
Parental phenotypes
Short tail, normal coat (hybrid)
x
Long tail, wavy coat (pure)
Parental genotypes (2n)
(SW) (sw)
x
(sw) (sw)
(Meiosis)
(sw)
(sw)
Gametes (n)
(SW)
(sw)
(sw) (sw)
(SW) (sw)
(sw) (sw)
(SW)(sw)
(Random fertilisation)
Offspring (F1) genotypes (2n)
Offspring (F1) phenotype
50% short tail, normal coat
(SW) (sw)
50% long tail, wavy coat
(sw) (sw)
Example:
41 short tail, normal coat
:
42 long tail, wavy coat
Ratio: 1:1

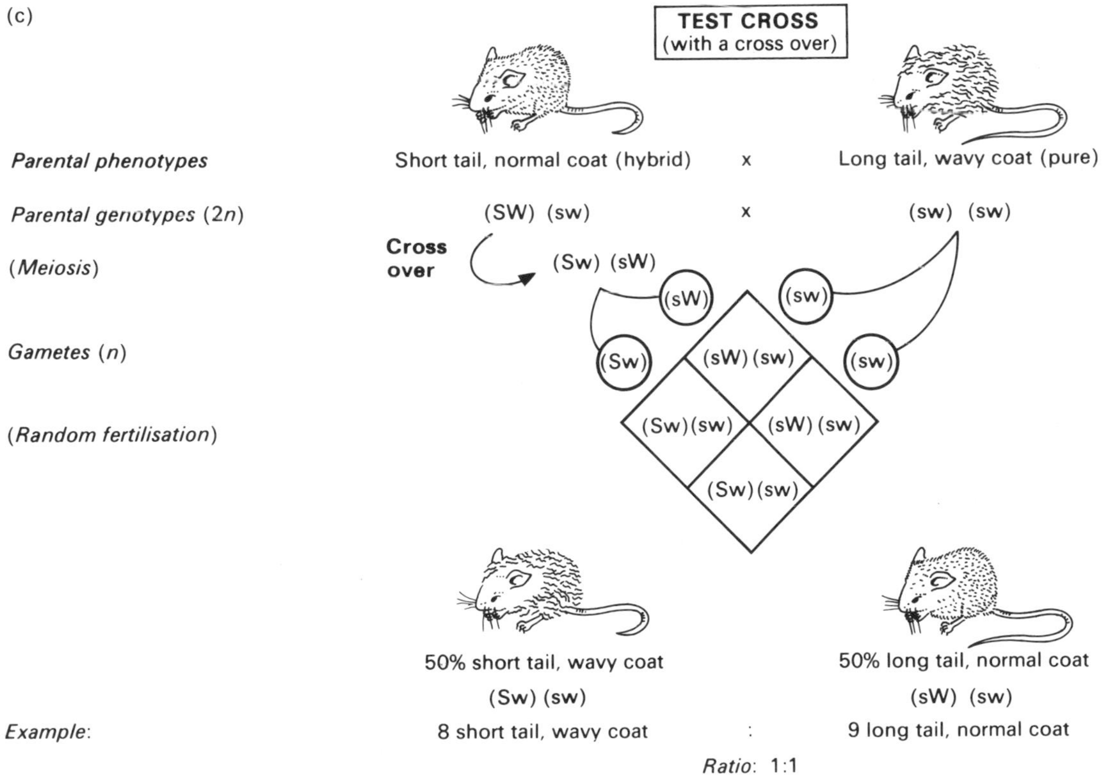
(c)
TEST CROSS
(with a cross over)
Parental phenotypes
Short tail, normal coat (hybrid)
x
Long tail, wavy coat (pure)
Parental genotypes (2n)
(SW) (sw)
x
(sw) (sw)
Cross over
(Meiosis)
(Sw) (sW)
(sW)
(sw)
Gametes (n)
(Sw)
(sw)
(sW) (sw)
(Sw)(sw)
(sW) (sw)
(Sw)(sw)
(Random fertilisation)
50% short tail, wavy coat
(Sw) (sw)
50% long tail, normal coat
(sW) (sw)
Example:
8 short tail, wavy coat
:
9 long tail, normal coat
Ratio: 1:1

Figure 6.9(b) and **(c)**

■ MAKING GENE MAPS

Chromosomes are made up of thousands of genes located next to each other rather like beads on a string. When chromatids cross over in meiosis, alleles on one chromatid are exchanged for different alleles on the other chromatid of the homologous pair. If two gene loci are some distance apart from each other, crossing over between them will tend to happen more frequently. This sort of chromosomal acrobatics makes it possible to map out the sequence and position of the gene loci. In an ambitious project called the Human Genome Project (see page 86), biologists are attempting to map all 46 human chromosomes. This is an extremely ambitious task but it will have incalculable benefit in the early diagnosis of genetic illnesses.

If you are able to work out cross-over values, you can make a chromosome map. Let's look at an example.

A plant has hairy stems and pink flowers. The alleles controlling these features are both dominant and are both found on the same chromosome. The homozygous recessive plant has smooth stems and white flowers.

A heterozygous hairy-stemmed, pink-flowered plant was crossed with the homozygous recessive and the following plants were grown from the seeds produced by the cross:

hairy stems and pink flowers = 44
hairy stems and white flowers = 5
smooth stems and pink flowers = 6
smooth stems and white flowers= 45

The plants with hairy stems and white flowers and the plants with smooth stems and pink flowers are the result of crossing over (work it out!).

Therefore, if a total of 11 plants in 100 are the result of crossing over, the cross-over value (or COV) between hairy stems and pink flowers is 11%.

$$\text{COV} = \frac{\text{No. of recombinants} \times 100}{\text{Total no. of offspring}}$$

Now suppose that you found that a third gene, one for pointed leaves, was also on the same chromosome. Breeding experiments like the one above might produce cross-over values as follows:

hairy stems and pointed leaves = COV of 18%
pink flowers and pointed leaves = COV of 7%

COV values would suggest that the sequence of genes is hairy then pink then pointed. By comparing the respective COV values of pink and pointed, and pink and hairy, a map can be drawn as shown in Fig. 6.10..

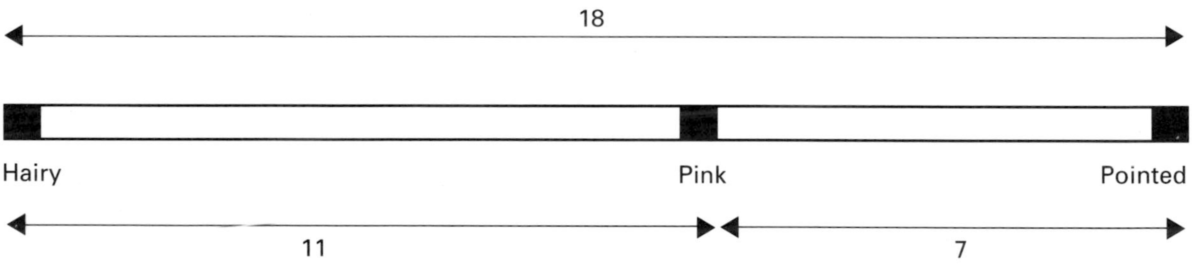
18
Hairy
Pink
Pointed
11
7

Figure 6.10 A simple gene map

■ MULTIPLE CHOICE QUESTIONS

Mice have a coat colour which is controlled by two genes (**C** for the presence of pigment and **A** for the colour of pigment produced). These genes are located on different chromosomes. When a black mouse was crossed with a white mouse, all the first generation were agouti (brown) and when they were interbred their offspring fell into the following ratio:

9 Agouti (brown): 4 white: 3 black.

Some of the possible genotypes are shown below.

A CCAA.
B CCaa.
C ccAA.
D Ccaa.

Select the genotype of the:

1. white parent.

2. black parent.

3. mouse which, when crossed with the double recessive, would produce only agouti progeny.

4. mouse which, when crossed with a mouse with the same genotype, would give only white progeny.

5. mouse which, when crossed with a mouse of the same genotype, would give only agouti (brown) progeny.

6. Bulb colour in onions is controlled by two genes located on different chromosomes. One gene determines whether or not colour is produced and has two alleles **C** and **c**. Presence of colour is dominant to its absence. A second gene determines the colour of the bulb and has two alleles **R** for red and **r** for yellow. Red is dominant to yellow. Find out the ratio and phenotypes from the cross

CcRr x **ccrr**

A 2 red: 1 yellow: 2 white.
B 1 red: 1 yellow: 1 white.
C 3 red: 3 yellow: 2 white.
D 1 red: 1 yellow: 2 white.

7. In the fruit fly Drosophila, four genes **P**, **Q**, **R** and **S** are located on the same chromosome. A series of test crosses gave these cross-over values:

PQ=8% **PR**=14% **PS**=4%
QR=22% **QS**=12% **RS**=10%

We can conclude that the order of genes along the chromosome is

A PQRS.
B SRPQ.
C QSPR.
D QPSR.

8. Examine the diagrams A, B, C and D below and decide which would result in the segregation of alleles **E**,**e** and **F**,**f** at anaphase 1 of meiosis?

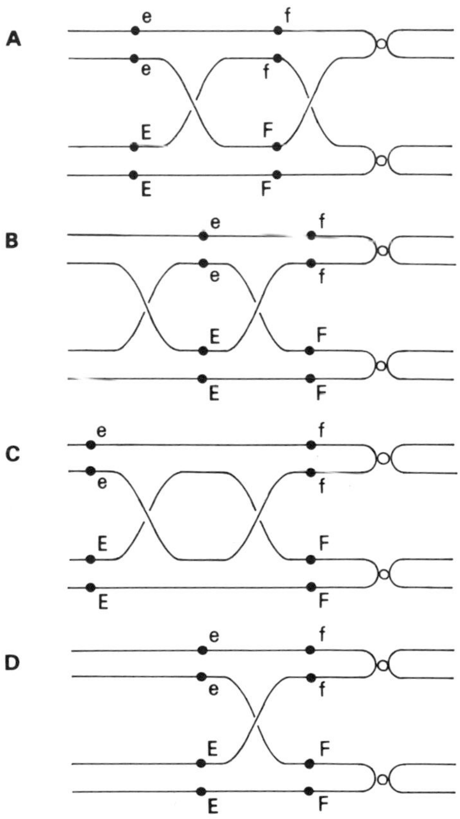
A
e
f
e
f
E
F
E
F
B
e
f
e
f
E
F
E
F
C
e
f
e
f
E
F
E
F
D
e
f
e
f
E
F
E
F

(See answers on page 98.)

CHAPTER 7

RATIOS, χ^2 AND HARDY-WEINBERG

INTRODUCTION

Understanding ratios is very important in genetics, and it might seem to you that there are an awful lot of them. The information in Table 7.1 might help you to recognise some of the genetic crosses that can give rise to particular ratios.

Sometimes it is difficult to identify a particular ratio because the number of offspring obtained is hardly ever spot on. For example, imagine a monohybrid cross in which only one of the parental genotypes is known. This parent is heterozygous **Aa** for one gene. The unknown genotype of the other parent could be heterozygous **Aa** or homozygous for the recessive allele, i.e. **aa**. 100 offspring are produced of which 41 show the phenotype of the dominant allele and 59 show the phenotype of the recessive allele. Is this a 3:1 ratio or a 1:1 ratio? If it is 3:1 it suggests that the unknown genotype is heterozygous but if it is 1:1 the unknown genotype is more likely to be homozygous recessive. Fortunately there is a statistical test that can help you. It is called the χ^2 (Chi squared) test. To understand how to use the test it is best to start by thinking about coins!

In theory, if you were to throw 100 coins into the air you might expect 50 to land on 'heads' and 50 to land on 'tails'. This is because each coin has a 1 in 2 chance of landing either way. Try it for yourself. You will probably find that the coins land in a ratio of heads to tails not far from the theoretical 50:50 ratio and any difference probably does not surprise or alarm you.

However, you would be very surprised if the coins landed with 100 on heads and none on tails at all. In fact, you would be positively suspicious that the coins were somehow biased. You might also be suspicious if the results were exactly 50:50 each time. Between the 50:50 expected ratio and the 100:0 unexpected ratio lie a vast number of other possible ratios and it is difficult to decide at what point the ratio you observed would suggest to you that the coins might be biased in someway.

This is where the χ^2 statistical tool can help you decide. The test is designed to tell you the probability of any difference between an expected result and an observed result being due to chance. It is not a complicated test and you do not need to understand the underlying mathematics that were used to derive it. After all, many of you will learn how to use a computer with little idea of how the computer works. All you need to do for χ^2 is learn how to apply the test and interpret the result.

The formula used to find the χ^2 value is:

$$\chi^2 = \Sigma \frac{(O-E)^2}{E}$$

Remember that in the example using coins there are two categories, i.e. heads and tails. This will help you to understand how the symbols in the formula are defined.

O = the number of observed results in a category.

E = the number of expected results in a category.

Σ = 'the sum of', and serves to remind you to repeat the calculation in the formula for each category being tested.

Look at the following example. A coin was tossed 100 times. The results were 40 heads and 60 tails. The χ^2 value can be calculated as follows:

Categories	*Heads*	*Tails*
Number observed (O)	40	60
Number expected (E)	50	50
$(O-E)$	−10	+10
$(O-E)^2$	100	100
$\frac{(O-E)^2}{E}$	$\frac{100}{50} = 2$	$\frac{100}{50} = 2$

$$\chi^2 = \Sigma \frac{(O-E)^2}{E} = 2 + 2 = 4$$

TYPE OF CROSS		EXAMPLE	EXPECTED PHENOTYPIC RATIOS
Genotypes	**Phenotypes**		
Rr x rR	Round x round seeds	Pea (heterozygous round-seeded self-pollinated)	3:1 round:wrinkled
Tt x tt	Tall x dwarf	Heterozygous tall pea x homozygous dwarf pea	1:1 tall:dwarf
IAIB x IAIB	AB x AB blood group	In man A and B are codominant in AB bloodgroup	1:2:1 group A : AB : B
RrYy x RrYy	Heterozygous round yellow-seeded peas	Round, yellow-seeded peas (F1 self-pollinated)	9:3:3:1 yellow round:yellow wrinkled:green round:green wrinkled
PpRr x pprr	Walnut x single comb	Test cross in chickens. Heterozygous walnut x homozygous single comb	1:1:1:1 pea:rose:walnut:single
RrBb x RrBb	Purple flowers	Heterozygous purple sweet peas self-pollinated	9:7 purple:white
AaCc x AaCc	Agouti x agouti	In mice A– = agouti if C is present, aa = black if C is present and – –cc = white	9:3:4 agouti:black:white
AaCc x aaCc	Agouti x black	In mice A–C– = agouti, – –cc = white and aaC– = black	3:3:2 agouti:black:white
AaCc x Aacc	Agouti x white	In mice - explanation as above	3:1:4 agouti:black:white
Yy x Yy	Agouti x agouti	In mice Y (yellow fur) is dominant to y (agouti) - but YY is a lethal combination and the fetus will die in the uterus	2:1 yellow:agouti (pure yellow YY will die in uterus)

Table 7.1

Whatever χ^2 value is obtained can be looked up in the special χ^2 tables (see Fig. 7.2). The degree of freedom is one less than the number of categories being investigated. In our example, there are two categories (i.e. heads and tails). Therefore, the degree of freedom is 1 (i.e. $n = 1$).

n	p = ·99.	·98.	·95.	·90.	·80.	·70.	·50.	·30.	·20.	·10.	·05.	·02.	·01.
1	·000157	·00628	·00393	·0158	·0642	·148	·455	1·074	1·642	2·706	3·841	5·412	6·635
2	·0201	·0404	·103	·211	·446	·713	1·386	2·408	3·219	4·605	5·991	7·824	9·210
3	·115	·185	·352	·584	1·005	1·424	2·366	3·665	4·642	6·251	7·816	9·837	11·345
4	·297	·429	·711	1·064	1·649	2·195	3·357	4·878	5·989	7·779	9·488	11·668	13·277
5	·554	·752	1·145	1·610	2·343	3·000	4·351	6·064	7·289	9·236	11·070	13·388	15·086
6	·872	1·134	1·635	2·204	3·070	3·828	5·348	7·231	8·558	10·645	12·592	15·033	16·812
7	1·239	1·564	2·167	2·833	3·822	4·671	6·346	8·383	9·803	12·017	14·067	16·622	18·475
8	1·646	2·032	2·733	3·490	4·594	5·527	7·344	9·524	11·030	13·362	15·507	18·168	20·090
9	2·088	2·532	3·325	4·168	5·380	6·393	8·343	10·656	12·242	14·684	16·919	19·679	21·666
10	2·558	3·059	3·940	4·865	6·179	7·267	9·342	11·781	13·442	15·987	18·307	21·161	23·209

Table 7.2 χ^2 (Chi squared) tables

Look at Table 7.2 and find the point where *n* (number of degrees of freedom) is 2. By moving horizontally along this degree of freedom you will come across a χ^2 value closest to the one you calculated using the χ^2 formula. Once you have found this value you move vertically upwards to a probability number. This is the number that tells you what the probability is of your observed results differing from your expected results by chance.

As a rule of thumb, scientists have decided that the $p = 0.05$ value represents a boundary. If a *p* value is greater than 0.05 it suggests that the difference between observed and expected results is very likely to be due to chance. If a *p* value is below 0.05 it suggests that the difference between observed and expected results is less likely to be due to chance and suggests that something else is the reason for the difference. In the coin example, the something else might be the fact that the coins are deliberately weighted on one side.

In our worked example, a χ^2 value of 4 with one degree of freedom is very close to the *p* value of 0.05. Therefore, a 40:60 coin-tossing ratio could be accepted as being due to chance.

Before using the χ^2 test you must decide on the idea or hypothesis you are testing. In this example, you are testing whether the presence of a head or a tail influences the way a coin will land after it has been thrown into the air. This idea has then to be expressed in a different way. You say that the presence of a head and a tail on a coin will *not* influence the way it will land after it has been thrown in the air! This different way of saying what idea it is you are testing is called the *Null hypothesis*.

1. Explain whether the results obtained in the genetic cross mentioned in the first paragraph on page 75 suggest whether a 3:1 or a 1:1 ratio is most likely.

2. The χ^2 test can also be used to help you explain how genes are inherited. For example, imagine an autosomal dihybrid cross between two Martians in which each gene has a dominant and a recessive allele. One of the parents is heterozygous for the first gene which controls height and for the second gene which controls colour. The other parent is homozygous recessive for both genes. 1000 offspring are produced, and at this point you do not know whether the genes are independently assorted or linked.

Let **A** = the dominant allele for the first gene, and let **a** = the recessive allele. Let **B** = the dominant allele for the second gene and let **b** = the recessive allele. The presence of **A** makes offspring tall, **a** makes offspring short; **B** makes offspring green and **b** makes offspring white.

The results of the cross are shown in Table 7.3. Use the results to explain whether or not you think the two Martian genes assort independently. If your answer is 'no' suggest how the results could have been produced.

Offspring phenotype	Number of offspring
Tall and green	300
Tall and white	200
Short and green	200
Short and white	300

Table 7.3

3. When Mendel carried out a cross between two heterozygous pea plants with round and yellow seeds, he obtained the following results

Yellow, round	315
Yellow, wrinkled	101
green, round	108
green, wrinkled	32
Total	556

Carry out a χ^2 test to see how closely this confirms Mendel's expected ratio of 9:3:3:1 . (See answers on page 106.)

HARDY AND WEINBERG

Two mathematicians called Hardy and Weinberg were able to show that, providing a number of assumptions were made, the frequency of the genotypes and the frequency of the alleles in a population would remain the same generation after generation.

They developed an equation to illustrate their point:

$$p^2 + 2pq + q^2 = 1$$

It looks a little frightening but is not too difficult to understand. What follows is an attempt to show you how the equation is derived.

Diploid ($2n$) animals have paired autosomes. Each locus is represented twice. If a locus is monomorphic, only having one functional allele (e.g. **A**), the population would be homozygous at that locus. For example,

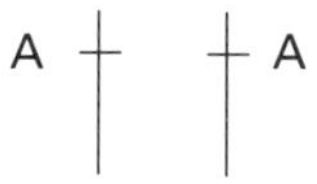
A
A

However, many loci are represented by more than one allele, i.e. the polymorphic situation. For example if you consider two functional alleles (e.g. **A** and **a**), there are three possible genotypes:

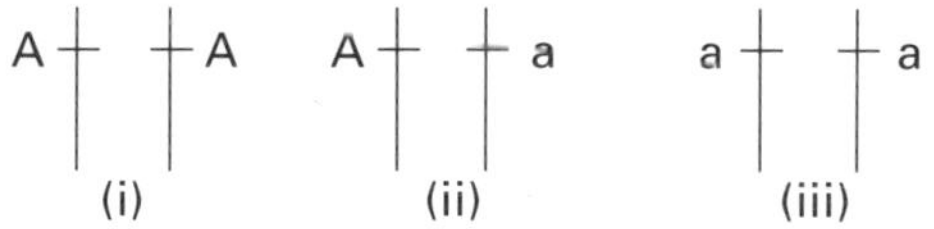
A
A
A
a
a
a
(i)
(ii)
(iii)

Imagine a parental generation which has individuals with these three different genotypes. The allele **A** and the allele **a** would each be present in the population at a particular frequency.

The frequency of a characteristic within any group can be expressed in many different ways. For example, in a group of 100 marbles containing 20 red marbles and 80 blue marbles, the frequency of red marbles can be shown as:

(i) 20/100 (ii) 1/5 (iii) 20% (iv) 0.2.

Similarly, the frequency of blue marbles can be shown as:

(i) 80/100 (ii) 4/5 (iii) 80% (iv) 0.8.

Regardless of the way the frequency is expressed, their sum must always be equal to 1. Thus:

(i) 20/100 + 80/100 = 1 (ii) 1/5 + 4/5 = 1

(iii) 20% + 80% = 1 (iv) 0.2 + 0.8 = 1

It is customary to represent the two frequencies by the letters p and q. Using the above reasoning, $p + q = 1$. In the biological example above you can now say that the frequency of allele **A** = p, whilst the frequency of allele **a** = q.

The Hardy-Weinberg equilibrium would have you believe that the frequency of these alleles will remain the same generation after generation. In order to find out what the frequency of these alleles will be in the next or daughter generation reproduction must take place. During reproduction haploid gametes are formed, and according to Mendel's principle of segregation, the alleles controlling a particular trait will be separated during gamete formation. Each gamete should only carry one allele of each pair. Only two types of gamete will be made by both males and females, i.e. either **A** or **a**. Below is a list of all the possible combinations of these gametes. The frequencies of the alleles and of the genotypes produced have been shown in brackets.

	Male gametes A(p)	a(q)
Female gametes A(p)	AA(p^2)	Aa(pq)
Female gametes a(q)	Aa(pq)	aa(q^2)

The frequency of the genotypes in the daughter generation can now be calculated as:

$$p^2 + 2pq + q^2$$

Note: $$p^2 + 2pq + q^2 = 1$$

(Here the 1 is equivalent to 100% of the offspring.)

You can now do some simple algebra to calculate the frequency of the alleles in the daughter generation. This will be the frequency of the homozygotes plus half the frequency of the heterozygotes.

For allele **A** this will be:

$$= p^2 + pq$$
$$= p(p + q) \text{ but } (p + q) = 1$$
$$= p(1)$$
$$= p$$

In the parental generation the frequency of allele **A** was also p and so there has been no change in the frequency of this allele from the parental generation to the daughter generation as predicted.

A similar analysis reveals the same is true for allele **a**:

$$= q^2 + pq$$
$$= q(q + p) \text{ but } (q + p) = 1$$
$$= q(1)$$
$$= q$$

So, the Hardy-Weinberg equation indicates that the frequency of alleles and the frequency of genotypes in a population will remain stable generation after generation. This also means that evolution would not occur. However, the equation depends on six assumptions:

- The population must be large;
- The population must be reproductively isolated, i.e. there must be no immigration or emigration;
- Mating between individuals must be random;
- There must be no difference in fertility between individuals;
- There must be no difference in rates of survival between individuals;
- There must be no mutations.

You can draw your own conclusions about the liklihood of evolution *not* occurring! Nevertheless, the Hardy-Weinberg equation is a very useful tool.

PROBLEM EXAMPLE

An animal can be hairy or hairless. The hairy allele is dominant to the hairless allele. 25% of the population are hairless. The frequency of the hairless genotype (i.e. q^2) is therefore 0.25.

With this kind of information it is possible to calculate the frequency of homozygotes and heterozygotes for hairyness as follows:

$q^2 = 0.25$, therefore $q = \sqrt{0.25}$

Frequency of homozygotes for hairyness = p^2

$$p + q = 1 \text{ but } q = \sqrt{0.25}$$
$$p + \sqrt{0.25} = 1$$

therefore $$p = 1 - \sqrt{0.25}$$
$$p^2 = (1 - \sqrt{0.25})^2$$

Frequency of hairy heterozygote = $2pq$

$$2pq = 2(1 - \sqrt{0.25})(\sqrt{0.25})$$

HARDY-WEINBERG PUT TO THE TEST

One use of the Hardy-Weinberg equilibrium is in calculating the possibilities of potentially harmful genetic crosses. Look at the following example.

About 16% of people in a population have Rhesus-negative (**Rh**-negative) blood. This does not present a problem until a woman who is **Rh**-negative becomes pregnant and carries a **Rh**-positive fetus. Small amounts of blood may pass from the fetus to the mother across the placental barrier resulting in the mother forming antibodies which may threaten the well being of the fetus.

Since a person with **Rh**-negative blood is homozygous recessive, the frequency of **rh** can be calculated using the Hardy-Weinberg equation.

The **Rh**-negative blood group **rhrh** can be represented as q^2.

$$q^2 = 0.16 \text{ (i.e. 16\% of the population)}$$

Similarly, the frequency of **Rh**-positive blood group **Rh** can be represented as p.

$$p = 1 - q \text{ but } q = \sqrt{0.16} = 0.4$$

therefore $p = 1 - 0.4 = 0.6$

The only way that the pregnant mother is likely to be at risk is if the father of the child is **Rh**-positive, and has passed on **Rh** to the fetus.

Rh-negative males cannot pass on **Rh** and so about 16% of marriages involving **Rh**-negative mothers will be to **Rh**-negative fathers.

Rh-positive males may be of two genotypes; **RhRh** or **Rhrh**. In the latter case, half of the pregnancies will result in a **Rh**-negative fetus anyway. So what are the risks?

RhRh males: $p^2 = 0.6 \times 0.6$

$= 0.36$

or 36% of the population

Rhrh males: $2pq = 2 \times 0.6 \times 0.4$

$= 0.48$

or 48% of the population

However, only half of the pregnancies with a **Rhrh** male will produce a **Rh**-negative fetus. So the risk would seem to be:

$0.36 + 0.24$

$= 0.6$

or 6% of all pregnancies with a **Rh**-negative mother.

Therefore, for all mothers it will be:

0.16×0.6

$= 0.096$

or 9.7% of the population.

In practice, problems only occur with a second or subsequent pregnancy. If the mother knows that she is **Rh**-negative and that her partner is **Rh**-positive, she can seek medical advice. It is possible to test the mother's blood during pregnancy to anticipate any problems and treat them. Women who are **Rh**-negative should be aware, but not alarmed, by these medical facts!

Q 1. The MN blood group system in Man depends upon the inheritance of one pair of alleles. In a sample of 1100 Chinese from Peking, it was found that the number of people with blood group M (genotype MM) was 356, with MN was 519 and with N (genotype NN) was 225.

(a) Calculate the frequencies of the two alleles and the expected Hardy-Weinberg genotypic ratios.

(b) Is the population in Hardy-Weinberg equilibrium?

(UCLES A-Level 1984) *(See answer on page 106.)*

Genetic counsellors use the Hardy-Weinberg equation to predict the chance of couples giving rise to an affected child. They can calculate how frequent the carriers of a genetic disease are in a population by comparison with those who already have the disease.

2. Use the Hardy-Weinberg equation to complete the table below.

Genetic disease	Frequency of those affected (p)	Frequency of carriers (2pq)
Albinism	1 in 20 000	
Alkaptonuria	1 in 1 000 000	
Cystic fibrosis	1 in 2 000	
Phenylkentonuria	1 in 25 000	

Table 7.4

■ MULTIPLE CHOICE QUESTIONS

1. A fatal disease of the pancreas is attributed to the presence of an autosomal recessive allele. Homozygous recessive individuals do not survive. 10 000 babies were born during one year and 4 died of the disease. This indicates that the frequency of the recessive allele is

A 0.98.
B 0.96.
C 0.04.
D 0.02.

2. A population of seals breed regularly on an isolated sand bank. Some of the seals have silver fur. Silver fur is due to a recessive allele. If 9% of the population of seals have silver fur, what percentage will be heterozygous for this gene?

A 58%.
B 50%.
C 49%.
D 42%.

(See answers on page 98.)

CHAPTER 8

DNA ANALYSIS: GENETIC FINGERPRINTING AND GENE TRACKING

Genetic fingerprint

Henry fingerprint

INTRODUCTION

In 1988, a man was sentenced to life imprisonment for his crime of murder. You might not think this is very surprising, but the fascinating thing about this case was the way in which his guilt was finally established.

For years forensic scientists have used the *Henry fingerprinting system* to help identify suspects. In this murder case, and for the very first time, police made use of a technique first called *genetic fingerprinting* (but more commonly called DNA profiling). By using it they earned themselves the title of DNA detectives!

The technique was developed by Professor Alec Jeffreys of Leicester University and the implications of its use have raised issues of concern to scientists, philosophers, lawyers and ethicists. All of the debate centres on a technique which allows scientists to look at the patterns of DNA we have inside our cells. It can be used to solve arguments over paternity, resolve immigration disputes, confirm animal pedigree and as mentioned earlier, it can be used to solve murder cases.

An extension of the technique also allows scientists to provide prenatal diagnosis of genetic disease by using a method called *gene tracking*.

GENETIC FINGERPRINTING

DNA can be extracted from any cell which contains a nucleus. Samples of blood, saliva, semen or the root of a hair can all provide ample amounts of DNA (only a small amount of the total DNA is used). Enzymes are added to the DNA which cut it up into millions of little pieces of unequal length. These enzymes are called *restriction endonucleases*. *Nuclease* because they cut nucleic acid; *endo* because they cut the nucleic acid *within* the DNA strand, not from the ends; and *restriction* because the cutting points are limited to highly specific recognition base sequences. These recognition sequences are usually 4-6 base pairs in length and are palindromes (i.e. one strand of DNA read from left to right carries the same sequence as the other strand read from right to left).

An example of a restriction endonuclease is EcoR1. This enzyme will only cut DNA where there is the following base sequence:

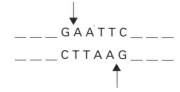

```
        ↓
___G A A T T C___
___C T T A A G___
              ↑
```

These cuts leave two exposed ends of DNA with the characteristic sequences:

___G AATTC___

and

___CTTAA G___

There are many types of restriction enzyme, each able to cut DNA at a different place. The place where the DNA is cut is called a *restriction site*. The size of the fragments is measured in kilobases (kb). One kilobase = 1000 DNA nucleotide bases.

Once the DNA has been cut with one or more restriction enzymes, the next step involves subjecting the fragments to *gel electrophoresis*. This is a process which makes the DNA fragments move along a sheet of gel by using an electric field. Shorter lengths of DNA will move further along the gel than longer lengths. At this stage, the DNA being used is double-stranded and has to be denatured to produce single strands for the next stage in the process. When this has been done the DNA is transferred to a sheet of nitrocellulose or nylon membrane by a process *called Southern blotting*. In this process, the membrane is sandwiched between the gel and sheets of blotting paper and the DNA moves across into the membrane by capillary forces. The position of the DNA can then be fixed on to the membrane by exposing it to ultra–violet radiation. The entire process is shown in Fig.8.1. The DNA, which is in many millions of single stranded fragments, is now ready for exposure (i.e. *hybridisation*) to a gene probe.

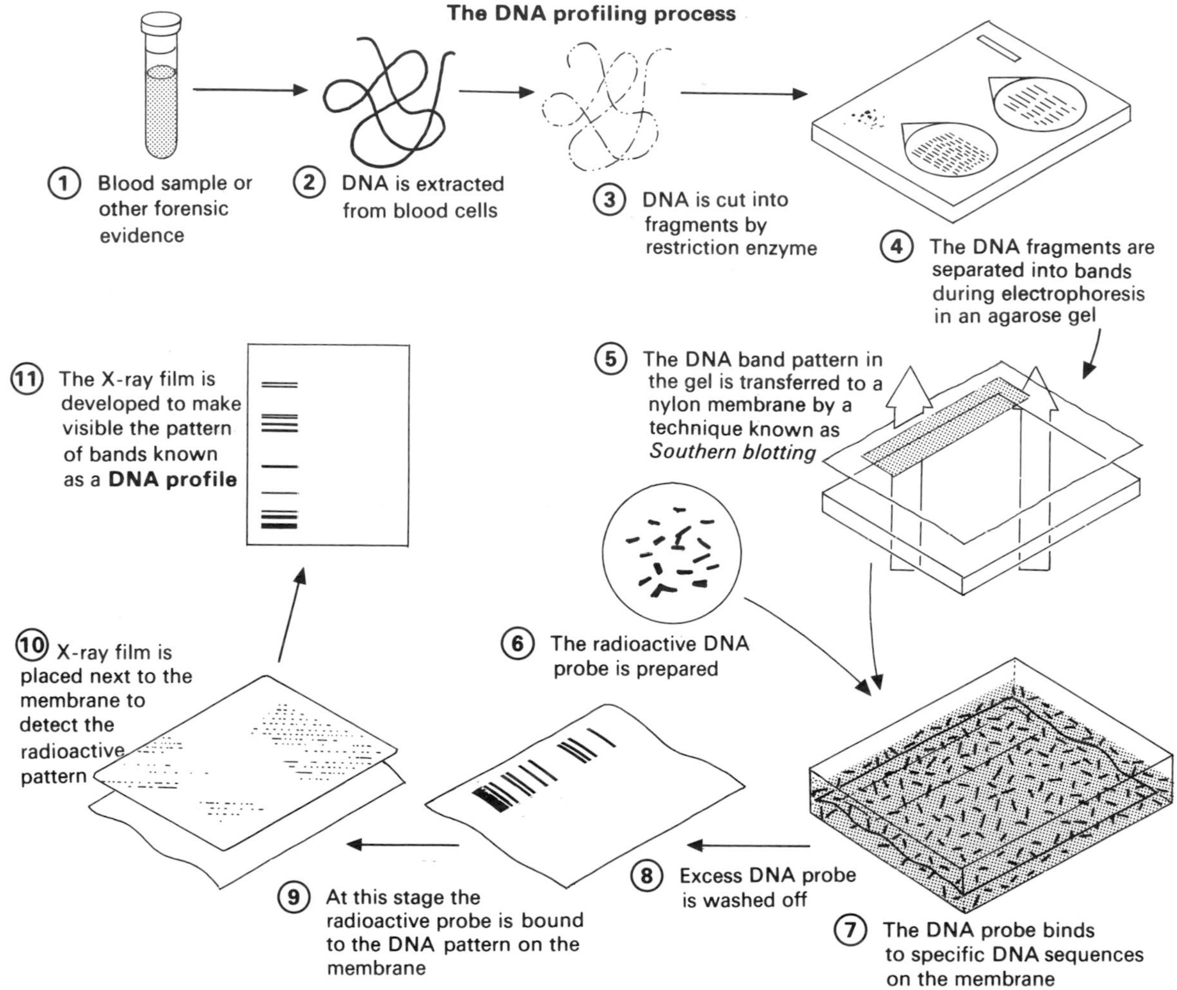
The DNA profiling process
1 Blood sample or other forensic evidence
2 DNA is extracted from blood cells
3 DNA is cut into fragments by restriction enzyme
4 The DNA fragments are separated into bands during electrophoresis in an agarose gel
5 The DNA band pattern in the gel is transferred to a nylon membrane by a technique known as Southern blotting
6 The radioactive DNA probe is prepared
7 The DNA probe binds to specific DNA sequences on the membrane
8 Excess DNA probe is washed off
9 At this stage the radioactive probe is bound to the DNA pattern on the membrane
10 X-ray film is placed next to the membrane to detect the radioactive pattern
11 The X-ray film is developed to make visible the pattern of bands known as a DNA profile

Figure 8.1 The sequence of events leading to the creation of a DNA 'fingerprint' or profile

A gene probe is simply a length of DNA which has been cloned to make many millions of copies. Each copy is a radioactively-labelled single strand of DNA. When a probe is added to the membrane it finds a complementary base sequence on the membrane and binds to it. Because the probe is radioactive, the recombined lengths of DNA show up as a pattern of dark bands stacked on top of each other when the membrane is exposed to X-ray film (see Fig.8.2).

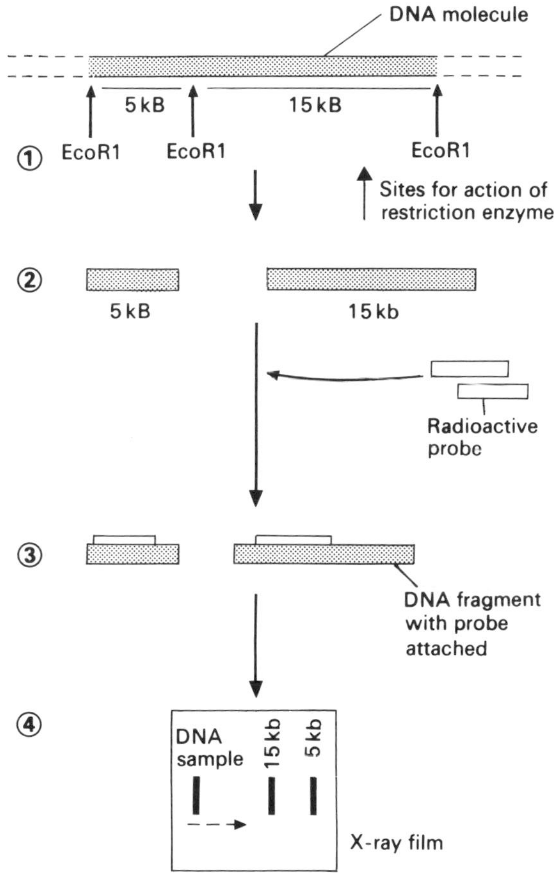
DNA molecule
5 kB
15 kB
①
EcoR1
EcoR1
EcoR1
Sites for action of restriction enzyme
②
5 kB
15 kb
Radioactive probe
③
DNA fragment with probe attached
④
DNA sample
15 kb
5 kb
X-ray film

Figure 8.2 How different lengths of DNA are displayed on X-ray film using a radioactive DNA probe

The pattern of dark bands obtained is determined by the size of the DNA fragments originally cut by the restriction enzyme. The size of these fragments is governed by the number and position of cutting sites which are recognised by the restriction enzyme.

We all have regions in our DNA which do not code for a protein. Such *nonsense DNA* follows the normal pattern of inheritance. The interesting thing is that these non-coding regions can have base changes which are harmless but which can produce new cutting sites for restriction enzymes or for that matter remove existing sites.

The vast range of different base sequences is an example of *DNA polymorphism.* Those base changes which alter the cutting sites of restriction enzymes are called restriction site polymorphisms, and they represent one way in which the size of the DNA fragments can vary between individuals.

Another way in which DNA fragments can vary in size depends on the number of times a specific base sequence in a non-coding region is repeated along a length of DNA. Some of us have a few repetitions, others have many. For this reason, these base sequences are called *hypervariable regions* (HVRs). As both restriction site polymorphisms and HVRs affect the size of DNA fragments they tend to be called *restriction fragment length polymorphisms* (RFLPs). These RFLPs are the basis for the genetic uniqueness of individuals as shown in genetic fingerprinting.

So, the banding pattern (rather like a bar code!) seen on the X-ray film depends on the length of the HVRs and the base sequences within. If the pattern produced by DNA found at the scene of a crime matches the pattern produced from the DNA of a suspect, evidence of guilt has been established.

Paternity cases are a little more complicated because the banding pattern from each parent will be different from the child, but there will be similarities as half the child's DNA will have come from the mother and the other half from the father. It takes enormous skill to be able to recognise these similarities.

GENE TRACKING

Gene tracking (which is even more complicated) is used to discover how harmful genes are inherited in families. In this process, scientists look at the DNA pattern from a specific chromosome of an affected individual and then study the DNA pattern of the parents to see if it is possible to see any difference between their chromosomes at the same gene locus. The process aims to provide prenatal diagnosis of genetic diseases.

There are not many DNA probes which can recognise the base sequence of a functional gene (i.e. a gene which has a DNA base sequence which determines the amino acid sequence of a protein molecule). Most probes in use today recognise the base sequence of a region linked to and close to a functional gene, but which is not itself involved in protein synthesis. These base sequences can have unique restriction sites called *polymorphic markers* and are very important because they tend to be inherited along with the base sequence of the functional gene (i.e. they mark the DNA near to where the functional gene is to be found). The closer a region containing a polymorphic marker is to the functional gene, the more useful it is when testing for genetic diseases.

The example shown in Fig.8.3 shows the typical results of a family where a harmful autosomal allele can be inherited. As you can see, there are lots of dark bands obtained using the probe.

In this example, both parents are known to be carriers of the recessive mutant allele because they have one child who clinically and biochemically has the disease. They also have a child who has no symptoms of the disease. When the mother became pregnant again they were worried that the fetus might be affected. In autosomal recessive inheritance, there is a 1 in 4 chance of this happening. By using a process known as *chorionic villus sampling* it is possible to obtain a sample of the fetal DNA for gene tracking.

The main task is to define the banding pattern of the affected child. It may then be possible to differentiate between the homologous chromosomes in each of the parents to find out which of the chromosomes carries the recessive allele.

In this example, one of the parental chromosomes has a unique restriction enzyme site (or polymorphic marker) in the region close to the gene locus for the normal and mutant allele. This chromosome is given the label Type 2. The parental chromosome lacking the restriction site is given the label Type 1.

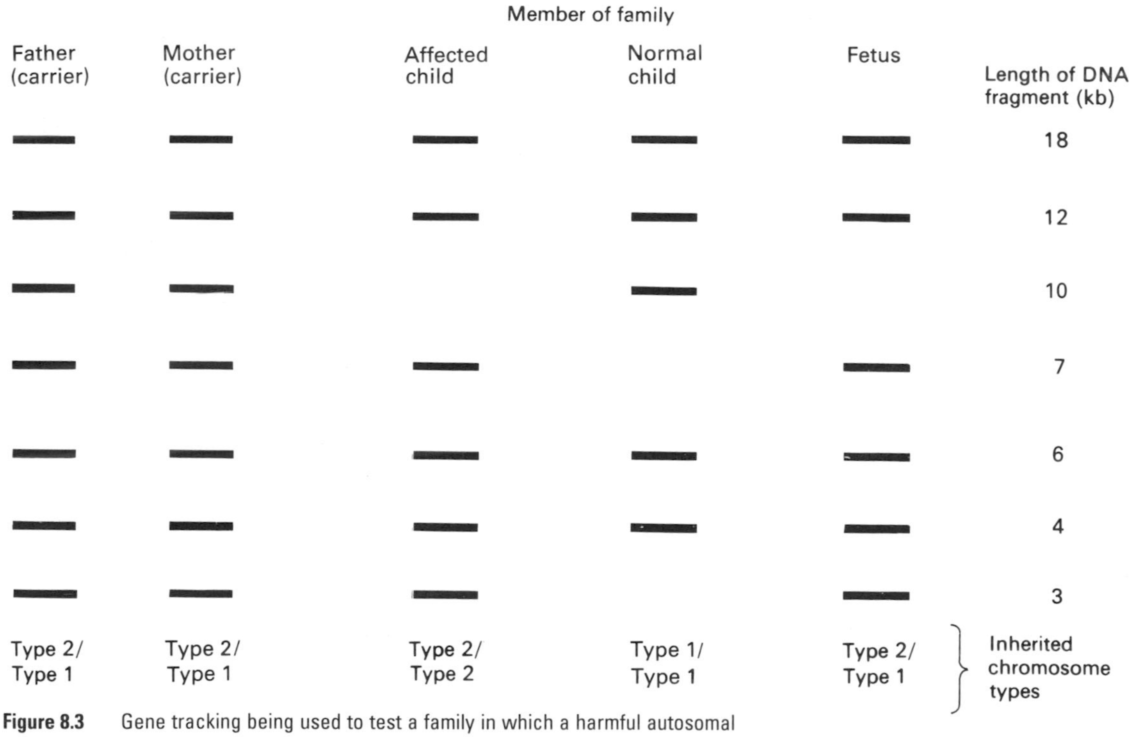
Member of family
Father (carrier)
Mother (carrier)
Affected child
Normal child
Fetus
Length of DNA fragment (kb)
18
12
10
7
6
4
3
Type 2/ Type 1
Type 2/ Type 1
Type 2/ Type 2
Type 1/ Type 1
Type 2/ Type 1
Inherited chromosome types

Figure 8.3 Gene tracking being used to test a family in which a harmful autosomal allele is inherited

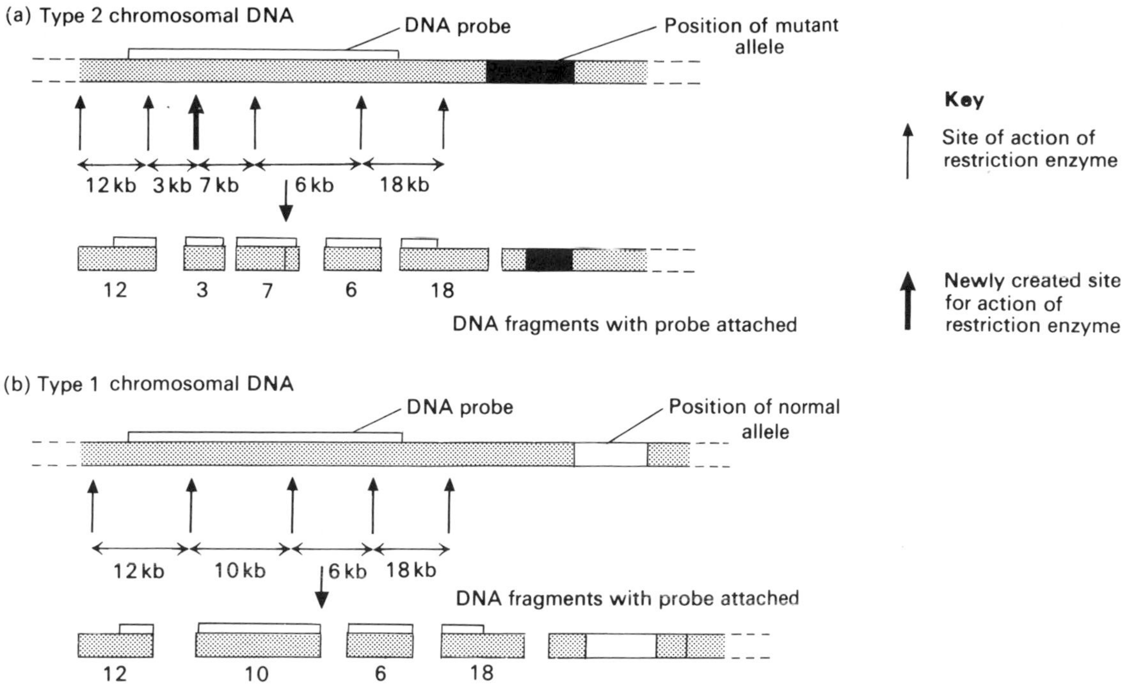
(a) Type 2 chromosomal DNA
DNA probe
Position of mutant allele
12 kb 3 kb 7 kb 6 kb 18 kb
12 3 7 6 18
DNA fragments with probe attached
Key
Site of action of restriction enzyme
Newly created site for action of restriction enzyme
(b) Type 1 chromosomal DNA
DNA probe
Position of normal allele
12 kb 10 kb 6 kb 18 kb
DNA fragments with probe attached
12 10 6 18

Figure 8.4 How Type 1 and Type 2 chromosomes produce different band patterns

DNA was obtained from key family members and digested with a restriction enzyme. Pieces of DNA of different lengths were obtained. Hybridisation with a radioactively-labelled probe (directed towards the Type 1/Type 2 chromosome) revealed band patterns for the parents, the children and the fetus (see Fig.8.3).

To understand how all the bands appear you will need to study Fig.8.4 carefully. This shows how the radioactive probe can make an entire length of complimentary DNA radioactive. As a result all the smaller pieces of DNA produced by the activity of the restriction enzyme will also be radioactive and will appear as dark bands on the X-ray film.

The position of the bands depends on the size of the DNA pieces which in turn depends on the number of places where restriction sites occur. These are shown by vertical arrows. The Type 2 parental chromosome has an extra restriction site which is shown by a heavier arrow. This means that two pieces of DNA (3 kb and 7 kb) will be produced from this region of the DNA fragment of this chromosome. In the Type 1 parental chromosome, however, the equivalent region of DNA does not have this extra restriction site, and so the restriction enzyme will produce only one piece of DNA which is10 kb in length.

All the other pieces of DNA produced by the restriction enzyme will be the same size in both the Type 1 and the Type 2 chromosomes.

If you look back at Fig.8.3 you will see that the affected child has both the 7 kb and the 3 kb band but lacks the 10 kb band. This suggests that the child inherited the Type 2 chromosome from both parents – clear evidence that the mutant allele must be present on this chromosome.

The normal child does not have the 7 kb or the 3 kb band, but does have the 10 kb band. This suggests that the child inherited the Type 1 chromosome from both parents and once again is clear evidence that the mutant allele is carried on the Type 2 chromosome.

Q 1. What chromosome type(s) has the fetus inherited?

2. Use the information to explain the genetics of this family. Make sure you explain the genotype of the fetus.

3. What banding pattern would you get if the normal child had been heterozygous?

Before getting too excited about the potential of genetic analysis we ought to reflect on the moral dilemma it creates. Gene tracking can show the quality of life people can look forward to. It can help people to make decisions based on fact rather than chance. For diseases like heart disease or diabetes, where genetic diagnosis cannot predict whether or not you will get the disease, but can hint that you are susceptible to it, a little knowledge could be of immense value – you could try to avoid the disease through exercise, diet or drugs.

You could argue that a negative test for some people would be greeted with great relief but what about the unlucky ones who produce a positive test? Should they be informed? Should their partners be informed? Should there be some legal restrictions over the use of routine blood samples in order to protect the individual? Is it right that we are in a position to have some choice over our children's genotype because diagnosis before birth is possible?

The Human Genome ("Hugo") Project is a multi-national effort by scientists to map the location and structure of all human genes. As work carried out by this group gathers momentum, these questions and many new questions will need to be answered.

Finally, to return to the murder case with which this chapter started. In order to solve this case, the police adopted a plan never before used in the history of forensic science. Believing the suspect lived in the area where the crime occurred, they took blood and saliva samples from all local males between 13 and 30 years of age (a range the police thought was sensible). Genetic fingerprinting cleared everyone living in the area of the crime, but there were still some people to test who had left the area since the crime had been committed.

The murderer, when asked to give a blood sample, convinced a workmate that he did not have the time to go and give it. The workmate took the test instead but was heard telling the story to friends later on in a pub. The information was passed to the police who interviewed the workmate. They then arrested the first man and blood and saliva samples sent for analysis showed that the DNA fingerprint perfectly matched that of the killer's - the murderer had been found!

Q Look at the DNA profiles in the photograph (top right). Can you determine which of the suspects was the murderer?

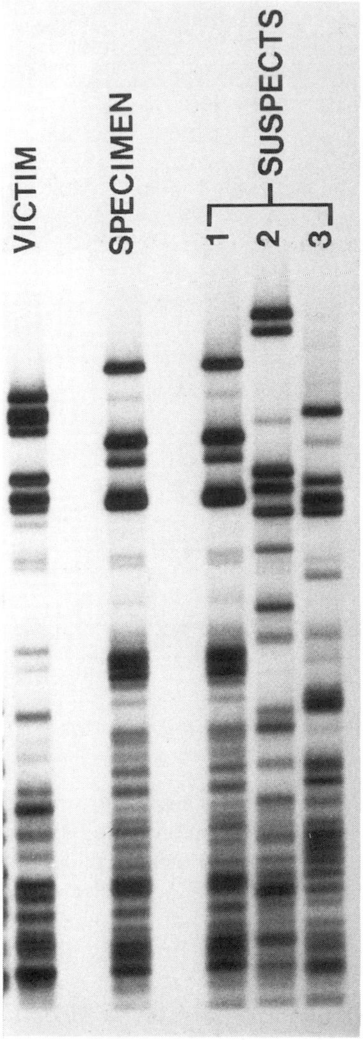
VICTIM
SPECIMEN
SUSPECTS
1
2
3

DNA from the scene of a crime and from three suspects

New applications of these DNA techniques are being developed in laboratories around the world. The presence of the bacteria *Listeria monocytogenes* in cultures of soft cheese can be detected using a DNA probe. This radioactive probe is specific for just this one species of Listeria – the one that is harmful to young children and pregnant mothers.

Another group of biologists are working on the DNA profiles of a colony of rabbits. They have found it possible to determine familial relationships and relate these to the social hierarchy of the colony. These are the most intensively studied rabbits anywhere, and as economically important pests and members of food chains, the potential benefits of such research are enormous.

■ HOW GOOD A DETECTIVE ARE YOU?

Look at the genetic fingerprints shown below and use them to answer the following questions.

Q 1. In Photo 1, which suspect do you think is guilty and left his bloodstain at the scene of the crime?

2. Which of the two men in Photo 2 is the true father of the child?

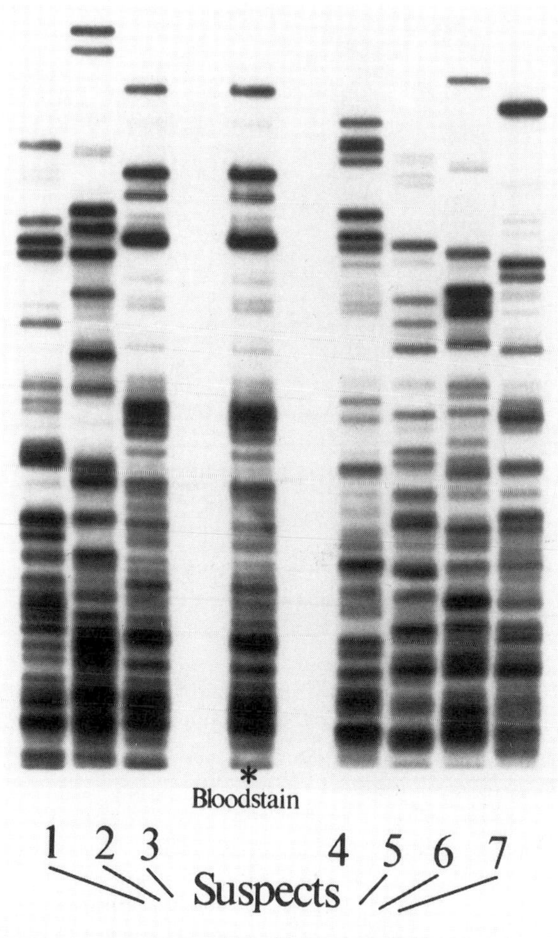

*
Bloodstain
1 2 3
4 5 6 7
Suspects

Photo 1 DNA from a bloodstain and from seven suspects

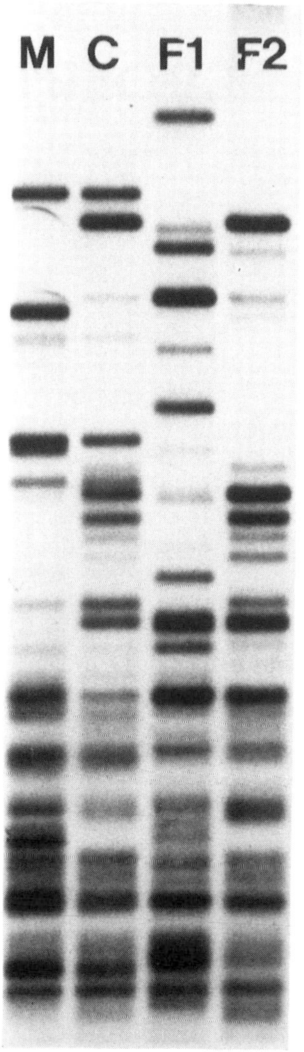

M C F1 F2

Photo 2 DNA profiles of individuals involved in a paternity case

CHAPTER 9

EVOLUTION

INTRODUCTION

The picture shown here may be of an unusually large family, but it does illustrate the point that humans do tend to produce far more offspring than are needed to keep the size of their population constant. This is why the size of the World's human population seems to be forever on the increase.

As can be seen in Table 9.1 many other *organisms have the potential to produce far more offspring than are needed to keep their population size constant* and yet the world does not appear to be swamped by them. Perhaps this is just as well. After all, even with the slow breeding of elephants one pair could produce 19 million descendants after 700 years. Space could become quite a problem!

Q Use Table 9.2 to calculate the reproductive potential of some familiar small mammals.

From a pair of	**Period of time**	**Potential number of descendents**
Cockroaches	7 months	1.6×10^{11}
Cod	1 year	9×16^{6} (eggs laid)
Fowl	1 year	280-300 (eggs laid)
Poppy plants	7 years	8.2×10^{31}

Table 9.1

Mammal	**Breeding age/weeks**		**Litter size**	**Gestation/days**	**Time after giving birth to next mating**
	Start	**Finish**			
Gerbil	12	78	4-6	27	Immediately
Guinea pig	16	78-104	3-5	60-72	Immediately
Hamster	10	52	5-7	16	1-8 days
Mouse	10	52	8-11	20	Almost immediately
Rabbit	24	104	4-6	31	35 days
Rat	12	52-65	9-11	22	Immediately

Table 9.2

Fortunately, the elephant problem never arises. Why is this? The fact that there is not enough food available to feed them all is one reason but there are other reasons. Predators and disease help to reduce numbers as does the availability of space. These various ecological factors all work together to resist the natural tendency for the population size to increase. They constitute what might be called *environmental resistance*.

Not all the organisms in a population are at risk from all aspects of environmental resistance. This is because in any sexually-reproducing population, meiosis has ensured that the individuals in a population will vary from each other. For example, some might be faster and thus escape predators. Taller tree-feeders are at an advantage when leaves become scarce at lower levels. Whatever the characteristics, one thing can be sure – they will vary among the individuals in a population. Those individuals *best adapted* to survive the environmental resistance will *survive*. The survivors will then be the ones who mate and produce offspring. Assuming the characteristic which helped the lucky ones to survive is genetic in origin, the favourable genes for the characteristics will also be passed to the offspring, thus giving them an advantage in their struggle for survival.

Charles Darwin was a natural historian and is credited with having thought out most of the ideas expressed above. He described the battle for life as the *survival of the fittest*. He did not mean it in the athletic sense of who can do the most press-ups, but rather in the sense of an individual possessing the most favourable characteristics to avoid being a loser in the contest for survival. Because the elements of nature tended to be the factors which tested which individuals were the best adapted, Darwin called the whole process *natural selection*.

Darwin further claimed that natural selection could be the mechanism by which the vast number of different species known on Earth could have evolved. His views, which became known as *Darwinism*, were published in his book *The Origin of Species* in 1859. He wrote this book on his return from a five year sea voyage on board HMS Beagle. This voyage allowed him to visit many lands and observe with his own eyes the vast array of life forms on the planet Earth. He could not believe that they were all invented by one Creator. He believed that they had somehow evolved from other living organisms and that natural selection had played a part in this. It was at this time that his theory of evolution was formed.

Charles Darwin

The Galapagos Islands 600 miles off the coast of Ecuador probably had the greatest impact on Darwin's thinking. During his five week visit in 1835, many of the organisms he saw on these mysterious islands were unique, having no counterpart on the mainland. The fact that the Galapagos Islands are volcanic in origin lends some support for Darwin's views on the Creation. At one time, these islands were well and truly submerged yet now they were flourishing with unique land fauna! What was created and what had evolved?

Another scientist, the Welsh plant collector and naturalist called Alfred Wallace, had made similar findings to Darwin but he became marginalised because he failed in the race to have his ideas published (although his explanation was read out at the same meeting as Darwin's account). At the time, neither Darwin nor Wallace knew of the existence of genes. More recent theories which attempt to explain the role of natural selection in evolution by referring to genes come under the heading of *Neo-Darwinism*.

NATURAL SELECTION IN ACTION

Darwin's theory depends on three observations and two inferences:

• Observation 1 Organisms produce more offspring than are needed merely to replace them (in favourable conditions);

• Observation 2 The size of a population remains fairly constant over a period of time.
Inference 1 There is a struggle for survival and some organisms die;

• Observation 3 All organisms display variation.
Inference 2 Those organisms best equipped for life will survive – hence the phrase *survival of the fittest.*

WHAT SORT OF EVIDENCE SUPPORTS DARWIN'S THEORY?

There are many famous examples of natural selection in action which will be briefly mentioned here. Some more unusual examples will also be described.

The peppered moth (*Biston betularia*)

The peppered moth is a famous example of natural selection. If you look at the insect collections made during the last century, examples of the peppered moth are quite common. These specimens are all light-coloured in the earliest collections. Later collections, however, show increasing numbers of dark-coloured (i.e. melanistic) moths. These became particularly common in industrialised areas.

Moths rest on the barks of trees with their wings open. The speckled pattern on the peppered moth's outstretched wings blends in with the lichen-encrusted bark of trees and so provides excellent camouflage. During the nineteenth-century, increasing industrialisation and pollution caused many of the lichens to die. (They are sensitive indicator species and die if the air contains acidic oxides, e.g. sulphur dioxide ($S0_2$) or oxides of nitrogen (NO_x)).

Light-coloured moths resting on the blackened bark are easy prey to birds but the darker, melanistic moths are less readily visible. Gradually, more melanistic moths were found in industrialised areas but in rural areas, the lighter form remained most common. With more strict pollution control in recent years, there is evidence of a resurgence of the light-coloured moth and a decline in the numbers of dark moths. Obviously, the peppered moth displays variation in wing colour and, depending on the selection pressure acting on it, one form will tend to be more successful than another in a given environment.

Peppered moth

The banded snail (*Cepaea nemoralis*)

A similar case of natural selection is illustrated by the banded snail *Cepaea nemoyalis.*

The shell of the banded snail displays a wide variety of both colour and banding. Snails found in the leaf litter in woodland tend to be brown and red whereas those found in the grassy hedgerows tend to be much paler, often yellow and with many bands. The banded snails are eaten by birds such as thrushes. Thrushes break open snail shells by striking them against a stone often called a 'thrush's anvil'.

Banded snails

In an experiment to demonstrate natural selection, a small spot of paint was placed just inside the lip of the shell (so as not to make the snail more visible to birds). Equal numbers of marked light and dark-banded snails were released in the leaf litter of a woodland. Over the next few days, shell fragments from around the thrush's anvil were collected and examined to see whether or not they were marked with paint. It was found that many more marked light-coloured snail shells were discarded around the thrush's anvil suggesting that there was a selective disadvantage for these snails in woodland.

When a similar experiment was repeated in grassland, more marked dark-coloured shells were found broken open near the anvil. Obviously shell colour conveys some selective advantage depending on where the snail lives. Shell colour also affects the time taken for snails to warm up and become active. Darker snail shells warm more quickly than light-coloured ones. This can affect the feeding activity of the snails. Light shell colour might well be of advantage in temperature regulation as the snails remain cooler in bright sunlight.

The effect of rainbow trout on brown trout

Rainbow trout (*Salmo gairdneri*) were unintentionally introduced once into a Scottish loch as a result of accidental damage to a cage in a fish farm. The loch formerly supported large numbers of the native brown trout (*Salmo trutta*). It was estimated that as a result the release of rainbow trout from the fish farm was about 2000 per year. Rainbow trout now outnumber brown trout in the loch by about 5:1. The loss of the brown trout is a cause for concern because the declining numbers represent a decline in the genetic diversity of the natural species (see Fig.9.1).

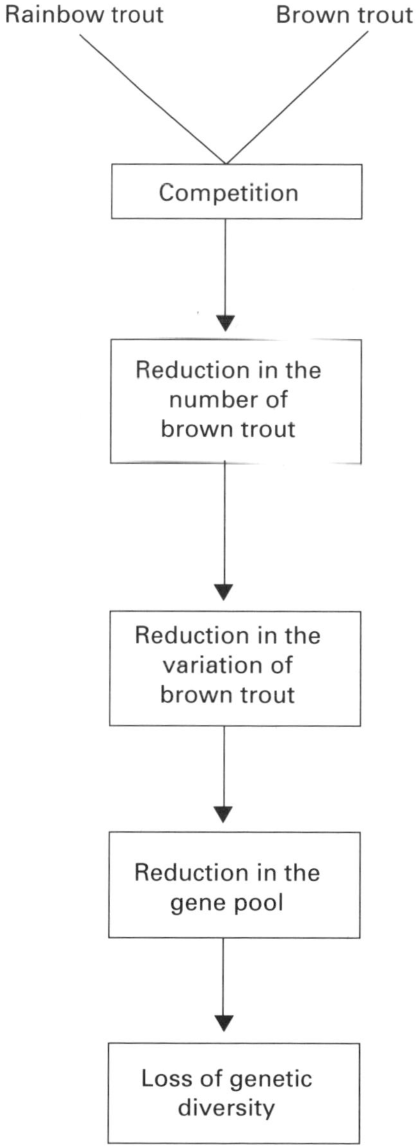
Rainbow trout
Brown trout
Competition
Reduction in the number of brown trout
Reduction in the variation of brown trout
Reduction in the gene pool
Loss of genetic diversity

Figure 9.1

Sickle cell anaemia and malaria

Sickle cell anaemia (see page 10) is due to the presence of an abnormal type of haemoglobin Hb^S instead of the normal haemoglobin Hb^A (see Fig.9.2). The trait is genetically determined and is recessive. In homozygous individuals (Hb^SHb^S), the abnormal haemoglobin causes the red cells to take on a crescent shape when oxygen is in short supply and the person becomes breathless and experiences pains in the muscles.

In severe cases, sufferers from sickle cell anaemia may even die, so there is a tendency for the gene to be selected against. Among Africans (and in Afro-Caribbeans) many people suffer from sickle cell anaemia, consequently there must be many more carriers of the disease (about 10%). It appears that sickle cell carriers have some resistance to the mosquito-borne disease malaria. Until the advent of anti-malarial drugs, parts of central Africa were known as 'the white man's graveyard', evidence that malaria is a life threatening condition.

The sickle cell anaemia/malaria situation is termed *balanced polymorphism*, the homozygotes being selected against while the heterozygote is being favoured.

OTHER EXAMPLES OF NATURAL SELECTION

There are other examples of genetic change that have been observed and studied in recent years:

- mosquito populations resistant to insecticides,
- bacterial strains resistant to antibiotics,
- rat populations unaffected by Warfarin (a rat poison),
- new plant strains able to survive in the presence of heavy metals in soil.

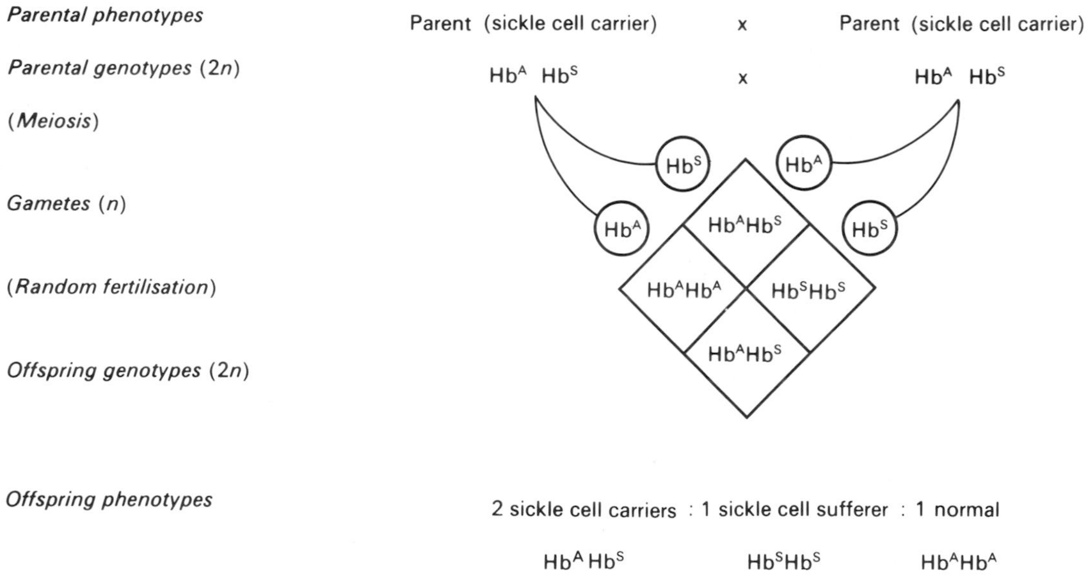

Parental phenotypes
Parent (sickle cell carrier)
x
Parent (sickle cell carrier)
Parental genotypes (2n)
HbA HbS
x
HbA HbS
(Meiosis)
Gametes (n)
HbS
HbA
HbA
HbS
(Random fertilisation)
HbAHbS
HbAHbA
HbSHbS
HbAHbS
Offspring genotypes (2n)
Offspring phenotypes
2 sickle cell carriers : 1 sickle cell sufferer : 1 normal
HbA HbS
HbSHbS
HbAHbA

Figure 9.2 The offspring of parents who are both carriers of sickle cell anaemia. Carriers (i.e. half the offspring) are favoured as they show no symptoms of sickle cell anaemia and have some protection against malaria. Sickle cell sufferers are selected against by sickle cell anaemia and normal offspring are selected against by malaria.

THE ORIGIN OF SPECIES

Darwin's theory of natural selection explains how natural variation can be exploited in different habitats. Eventually, distinct forms begin to appear, each adapted to their particular surroundings. This process is often called *adaptive radiation*. If the breeding populations become isolated for long enough they may well differentiate into distinct species. Darwin noticed this phenomenon on the Galapagos Islands where each island had its own unique flora and fauna (see Fig.9.3).

A group of finches – though obviously closely related to each other – demonstrated this gradual development of new species. Each of the Galapagos Islands had its own type of finch. The feeding and nesting habits of the birds differed from island to island. Natural selection, working in its own unique fashion on each island, favoured finches with different shapes and sizes of beak. Because the birds seldom journeyed from one island to another, the gene pool of each group of birds became different.

One of Darwin's finches

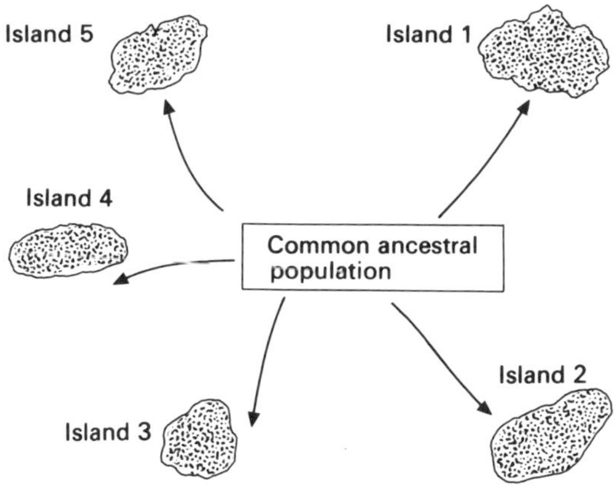

Island 5
Island 1
Island 4
Common ancestral population
Island 2
Island 3

Figure 9.3 Isolated populations on different islands will be subject to different environments

Clones and clines

A group of organisms with identical genetic characteristics is termed a *clone*, whereas a *cline* is a group of organisms which displays a range of characteristics going from one form to another. Clines occur where an organism has quite a widespread and continuous distribution in nature. The coat colour and body mass of many small rodents and insectivores (mice and shrews) demonstrate this sort of variation. Generally the colder the environment, the larger are the specimens since a large size has a favourable ratio of surface area to mass enabling the animal to conserve heat (and to store more fat). A possible explanation for this variation is the existance of *polygenes* (see Fig.9.4). Suppose there are five genes determining sizes, i.e. S^1-S^5 and that these genes can be present in dominant and recessive conditions. The largest animals will have the genotype

$$S^1S^1S^2S^2S^3S^3S^4S^4S^5S^5,$$

the smallest will be

$$s^1s^1s^2s^2s^3s^3s^4s^4s^5s^5.$$

Assuming a random distribution of the five pairs of alleles the number of small animals will be

$$(\tfrac{1}{2} \times \tfrac{1}{2} \times \tfrac{1}{2} \times \tfrac{1}{2} \times \tfrac{1}{2})^2$$

of the population a very small proportion! The chance of a $s^1s^2s^3s^4s^5$ gamete is one in 32 – so the chance of a homozygous recessive zygote will be about one in a thousand! If natural selection favours the recessive forms of the genes, this proportion will increase - this is what happens in a cline.

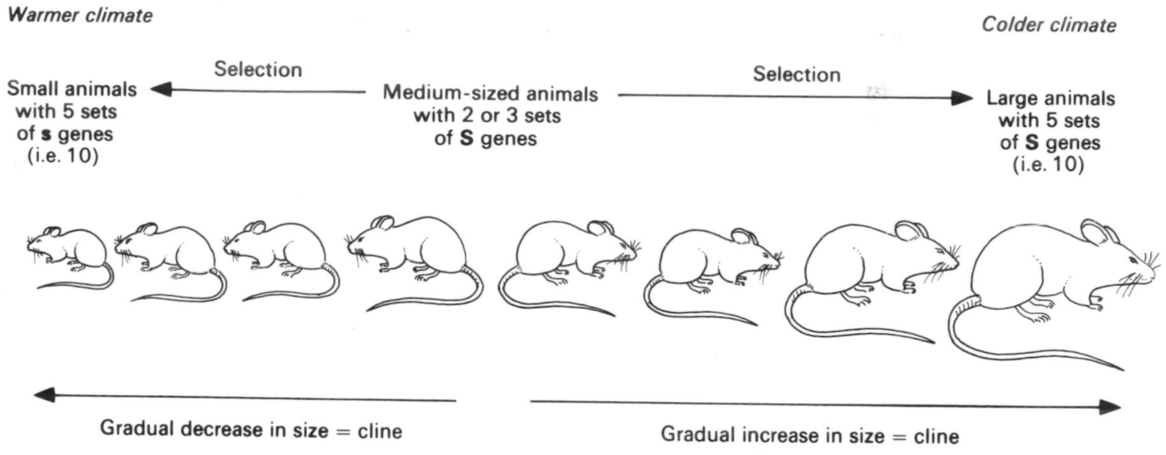
Warmer climate
Colder climate
Selection
Selection
Small animals with 5 sets of s genes (i.e. 10)
Medium-sized animals with 2 or 3 sets of S genes
Large animals with 5 sets of S genes (i.e. 10)
Gradual decrease in size = cline
Gradual increase in size = cline

Figure 9.4 How clines are formed

Genetic drift

Using the examples of the finches and the rodents, it is possible to see how variation and natural selection can cause a change in the composition of the gene pool. Although reproduction can occur by matings between 'neighbours' in the cline, the extreme forms might never meet up in order to breed. If they are isolated for long enough, the extreme forms might constitute new species.

An example of extremes comes from an interesting study of the effect of the domestic cat (*Felix catus*) on the native wildcat (*Felix sylvestris*).

Cats are descended from a common ancestor. It is thought that domestic cats were introduced into Britain by the Normans. Prior to that, the only cats in Britain were the native wildcats. By 1900, the only native wildcats remaining were restricted to the Scottish Highlands. Feral domestic cats (domestic cats which escaped from their owners and became wild) have distinct chromosome markers typical of their North African ancestors. Normally, distinct species do not interbreed, but when one is relatively common and the other extremely rare, hybridisation tends to occur. Perhaps the native wildcat finds it difficult to find a similar mate and so accepts a feral mate. In any case, the effect is to dilute the native wildcat genome with that of the feral cat. This might well be a case of one species causing the extinction of another closely related one!

Similar disasters may face native red squirrels in Britain. The grey squirrel was introduced to Britain several times from 1876 onwards. Grey squirrels can live at higher densities than red squirrels and exploit food both on the ground and in trees. As a result, the grey squirrels have caused a dramatic decline in the red squirrel population. Only in isolated Scots pine woodlands and on Brownsea Island in Poole Harbour are the native red squirrels thriving.

Red squirrel

THE ORIGIN OF SPECIES

Charles Darwin (1809 - 1882) was by no means the first to put forward ideas of evolutionary change from older and simpler forms to more complex organisms. However, he appreciated the fact that during sexual reproduction *variation* is generated and he wrote about '*descent with modification*' providing a variable population to be acted on by natural selection. Others had written about evolution, including his grandfather, Erasmus Darwin who wrote a textbook in rhyming couplets such as:
"Nurs'd by warm sunbeams in primeval caves
Organic Life began beneath the waves."
One famous biologist, Jean-Baptiste Lamark (1744-1829) was on the right track in spotting that the environment could have an important effect changing the phenotype of the individual but he wrongly assumed that the acquired changes would be inherited. His theory was at once rejected because in proposing change and improvement (which could be applied to humans), Darwin challenged the accepted social and religious order at a time of dangerous revolution in France. Subsequently, scientists also rejected most of Lamark's work because of the understanding that a phenotypic change was unlikely to cause an appropriate change in the coded message of the DNA.

When at the age of 22, Darwin started his voyage on *The Beagle* he was already an accomplished naturalist and collector and was influenced by the work of Malthus (*Essay on the Principles of Population*, 1778) and by some of the leading scientists of the day, such as Professors Sedgwick (Geology) and Henslow (Botany). He was well prepared to understand the significance of the observations he was to make on the five year voyage. He became fascinated by fossils, geological structures and the variations in flora and fauna and kept copious notes and diaries which on his return were converted into the first of a long series of publications. However, his growing convictions about evolution were too dangerous to discuss and for 20 years he wrote a secret notebook - frightened that his ideas would be condemned as both sacrilege and sedition. Eventually he was persuaded to publish, because Wallace (1823-1913) had reached the same conclusions about Natural Selection. His book *On the Origin of Species by Means of Natural Selection* was oversubscribed on the day of publication for the edition of 1250 copies.

Darwin had collected evidence for evolution from studies of biogeography, taxonomy, palaeontology, morphology and embryology and also from plant and animal breeding programmes.

Biogeography

On his travels Darwin had observed in similar climates (Australia, South Africa and South America) very different plants and animals. He dismissed the ideas of a special creation of each of the species and used his data as evidence for 'descent with modifications' in the different regions. His collection of finch-like birds from the Galapagos Islands was to become a convincing piece of evidence. These oceanic islands of volcanic origin had their own species of finch distinct for particular islands. They showed variations in size, type of beak and feeding and nesting behaviour. "Why should the species which are supposed to have been created in the Galapagos, and nowhere else, bear so plainly the stamp of affinity to those created in America?" he wrote; and in answer suggested that the islands were colonised from the mainland followed by descent with modification.

Taxonomy

Before the publication of *On the Origin of Species*, Darwin felt that he had to get to get to grips with the classification and taxonomy of a large and difficult group of organisms. He spent nine years on a detailed and complex study of the barnacles of the world and became convinced that the common characteristics in this group indicated inheritance from a common ancestor.

Palaeontology

The keen geologist and 'fossil hunter', Darwin, was excited by the South American fossils that he found. The skull of a "rhino-sized rodent" convinced him that organisms now extinct must have been replaced by their modified (evolved) relatives and descendants. (The fossil history of the horse is well established and shows clear evolutionary development over a period of 54 million years.)

Morphology, anatomy and embryology

Embryologists had long marvelled at the similar appearance of early stages of the embryos of mammals, birds and reptiles. But to Darwin, once again, it was evidence of descent from common ancestors. This was also his explanation of homologies, i.e. similar structures with different functions. Examples of homologous structures are seen in the limb bones of mammals; used for flight in the bat's wing , swimming in the seal's flipper and running in the horse's leg.

Breeding experiments

Darwin kept different varieties of pigeons and doves and met and corresponded with breeders around the country. He wrote about the artificial selection different breeders employed to select the best varieties of doves, dogs, cattle and flowering plants. These changes could be produced over a fairly small number of generations. It was, for him, a short step to the proposal of natural selection.

MODERN EVIDENCE

If only Darwin had known about Mendel's work *and* about DNA! We know that the same code is used in all organisms to make proteins. We also know that similar proteins are made in closely related organisms. A good example is myoglobin, the protein with a chain of about 150 amino acids. Its structure has been determined in a number of primates and it is interesting to note that there is only one amino acid difference between human and chimpanzee myoglobin. There is another single difference between human and gorilla myoglobin and only two differences between gorilla and chimpanzee myoglobin. The suggestion of a link between these three primates is also suggested by the identical alpha and beta haemoglobin chains of humans and chimpanzees. An enzyme in the respiratory chain, cytochrome c, is identical in human and chimpanzee metabolism and differs in only one amino acid from that in the rhesus monkey. A similar enzyme structure has been found in fungi, bacteria, plants and a range of animals.

There is also a growing body of evidence from studies of immunology where relationships can be established depending on antigen-antibody reactions. DNA-profiling (genetic fingerprinting) suggests future lines of research.
One of the things that delayed Darwin's publication of his theory was his fear of the reaction of academic churchmen to his ideas on "the descent of Man". In fact, after some ridicule, both church and state accepted and honoured him (he was buried in Westminster Abbey - an agnostic!). His colleague, Wallace, could never accept that the human brain could have developed by natural selection. Today we are more comfortable about discussing human evolution and, in fact, our close relationship to a number of species is seen as a means to solving a number of medical problems.

IS EVOLUTION CONTINUING TODAY?

We certainly find many examples of population groups, divided from each other and isolated in breeding groups, where changes are happening. Svalbard, isolated from Norway since glaciation has a separate sub-species of reindeer. A number of islands around the British coast have isolated populations of their own small mammals, e.g. Islay and Skomer shrews; Jersey, Skomer, Mull and Raasay bank voles. There are also many examples of variation leading to selection of individuals better adapted to survive and breed in changed environmental conditions, e.g. the melanic form of the peppered moth; plants able to grow on polluted mining spoil heaps; microorganisms rapidly evolving to meet new challenges and the influences of humans on domestic and wild species.
Some of the main questions are still to be answered but we are starting to get a better understanding of the ways in which organisms change and how the advantageous variations can be selected leading to better adapted individuals and populations.
Recently the geneticist, Theodosius Dobzhansky (1900-1975) wrote: "*Nothing in biology makes sense except in the light of evolution*". The science of molecular genetics and evolution is at an exciting stage of growth and fascinating developments in applied aspects of biology can confidently be expected during the next decade or so.

MULTIPLE CHOICE QUESTIONS

1. An interbreeding population of small mammals became geographically isolated on two separate islands. Each island provided different conditions which subjected the mammals to different selective pressures. After a long period of isolation, one group of mammals was introduced into the habitat of the other.
Which of the following would provide the best evidence of the formation of two distinct species?

A They each displayed new genes with altered base sequences.
B They had developed different amounts of fur with their own unique colouration.
C No fertile F_1 hybrids were produced.
D The two populations had not been able to interbreed due to a long period of isolation.

2. Which of the following forms of selection would result in the most rapid removal of a recessive allele from a population?

A selection against phenotypes displaying a dominant characteristic.
B selection against homozygotes.
C selection against heterozygotes.
D selection against phenotypes displaying a recessive characteristic.

3. The enzyme cytochrome c oxidase exists in a wide variety of organisms. This enzyme plays an important role in aerobic respiration. The precise amino acid sequence of this enzyme varies from species to species. These changes are a result of mutation and reproductive isolation.
Six different species 1, 2, 3, 4, 5 and 6 were compared. The numbers of differences in their amino acid sequences are summarised in the chart below.

	1	**2**	**3**	**4**	**5**	**6**
1	0					
2	5	0				
3	12	9	0			
4	22	20	16	0		
5	24	23	18	11	0	
6	23	25	21	9	2	0

Which of the diagrams A, B, C or D below indicates the most likely evolutionary relationships between the six organisms?

(See answers on page 98.)

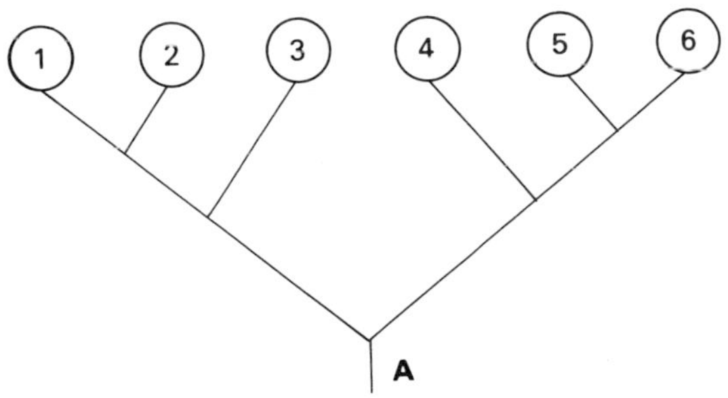
1
2
3
4
5
6
A

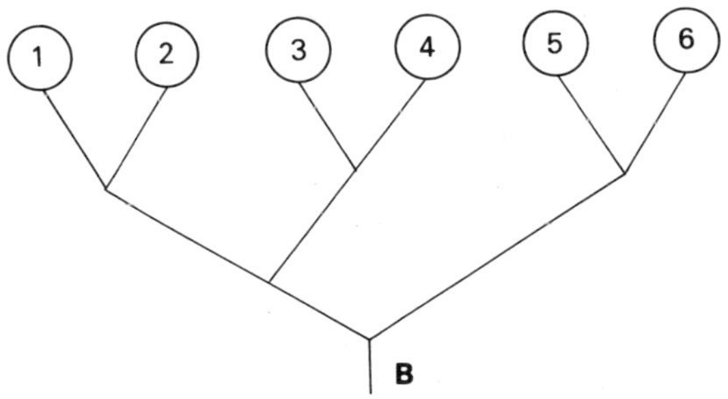
1
2
3
4
5
6
B

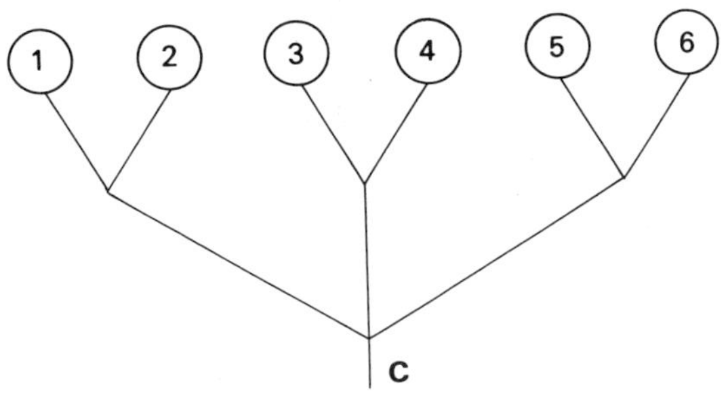
1
2
3
4
5
6
C

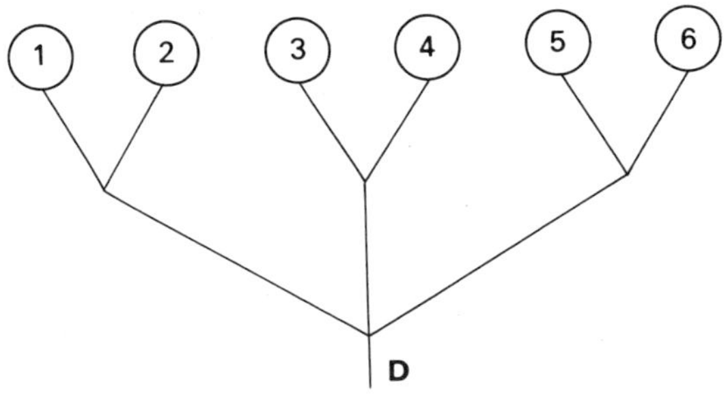
1
2
3
4
5
6
D

A ANSWERS

MULTIPLE CHOICE QUESTIONS

Chapter 1	Chapter 2	Chapter 5	Chapter 6	Chapter 7	Chapter 9
1 = B	1 = C	1 = B	1 = C	1 = D	1 = C
2 = B	2 = C	2 = B	2 = B	2 = D	2 = D
3 = B	3 = A	3 = E	3 = A		3 = A
4 = A		4 = B	4 = C		
5 = D		5 = B	5 = A		
6 = B			6 = D		
			7 = D		
			8 = C		

TEXT QUESTIONS

Chapter 1 page 19

1. Third generation DNA *ratio* light DNA : hybrid DNA 6 : 2 or 3 : 1

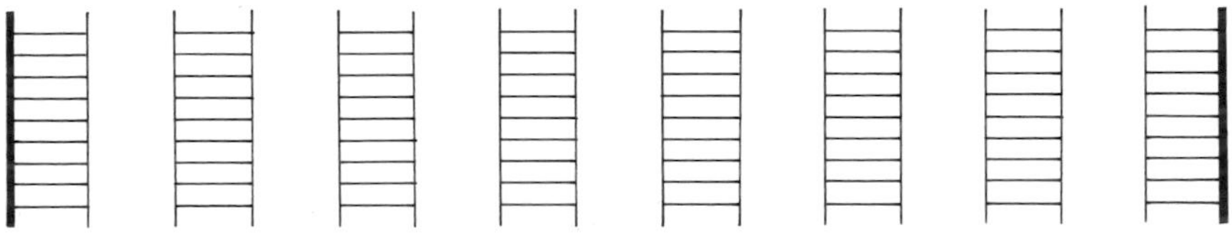

6 light DNA: 2 hybrid DNA

Ratio: 3:1

Chapter 2 page 26

1. Yes. Although the success rate decreases if the donor nucleus comes from an older cell. Some embryos continue to develop fully showing that the nucleus from the differentiated cell is still capable of coding for an entire organism.
2. They would all develop normally.
3. The data and graph indicate that, as there is progressively less success with donor nuclei from differentiated, older embryos, some genes may be switched off. The evidence shows that it is possible for some embryos to develop normally when the donor nucleus is from a differentiated embryo. This suggests that the mechanism controlling gene action is quite complex.

Chapter 4 page 42

2. (a) *Ratio* pink : white 1 : 1
   (b) *Ratio* pink : red 1 : 1

Chapter 4 page 43

3. *Ratio* brown : black 3 : 1
   But the genotype ratio will be
   BB : Bb : bb 1 : 2 : 1

Chapter 5 page 55

I^A and I^B are codominant, I^O is recessive

Chapter 5 page 56

2. Universal donor (O), universal recipient (AB)

Chapter 5 page 58

1. *A 'fowl' problem*
M = allele for melanin production
m = allele for lack of melanin

Since blacks possess melanin and are pure breeding genotype = MM
Splashed-whites cannot make melanin, so pure breeders = mm

Key Female = ♀ Male = ♂

(a)

Ginger ♀ x Black ♂

X^GX^G x X^BY

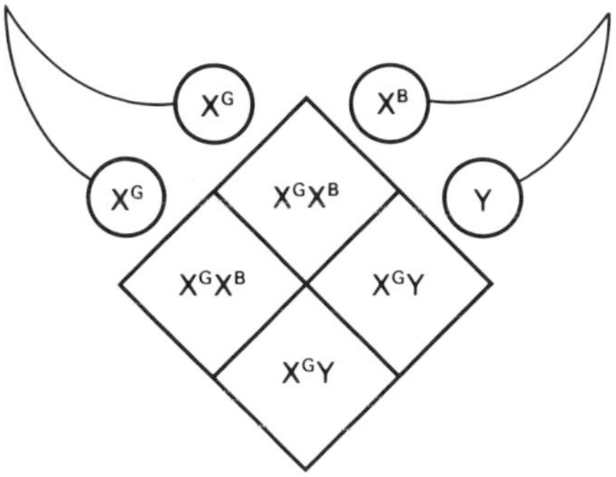

XG
XG
XB
Y
XGXB
XGXB
XGY
XGY

2 tortoiseshell ♀ : 2 ginger ♂
X^GX^B X^GY

(b) (i)

Black ♀ x Ginger ♂

X^BX^B x X^GY

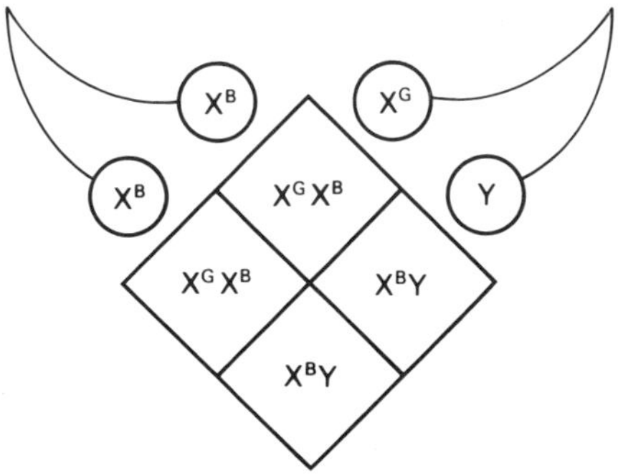

XB
XB
XG
Y
XG XB
XG XB
XBY
XBY

2 tortoiseshell ♀ : 2 black ♂
X^GX^B X^BY

(b) (ii)

Tortoiseshell ♀ x Ginger ♂

X^GX^B x X^GY

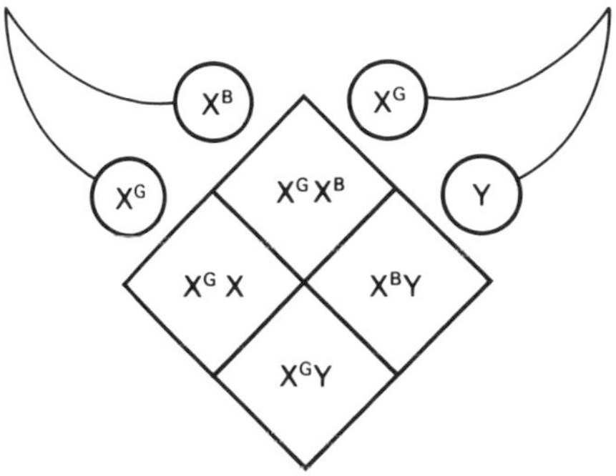

XB
XG
XG
Y
XG XB
XG X
XBY
XGY

1 ginger ♀ : 1 ginger ♂ : 1 tortoiseshell ♀ : 1 black ♂

(b) (iii)

Tortoiseshell ♀ x Black ♂

X^GX^B x X^BY

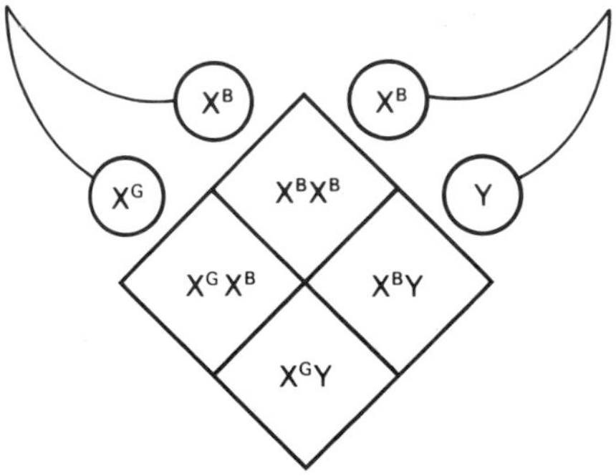

XB
XG
XB
Y
XBXB
XG XB
XBY
XGY

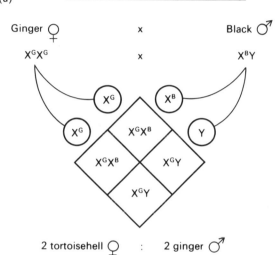

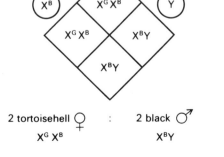

1 black ♀ : 1 black ♂ : 1 tortoiseshell ♀ : 1 ginger ♂

2. *Pink Antirrhinums*

(a) Since the pink antirrhinums fail to breed true, they must have more than one allele. The appearance of white and red flowers in the first generation suggests codominance.
Suppose pink = red and white information.
Therefore, C (for colour) exists as: CR (red) or CW (white)
Pink antirrhinum = CRCW

Pink flowers x Pink flowers

C^RC^W x C^RC^W

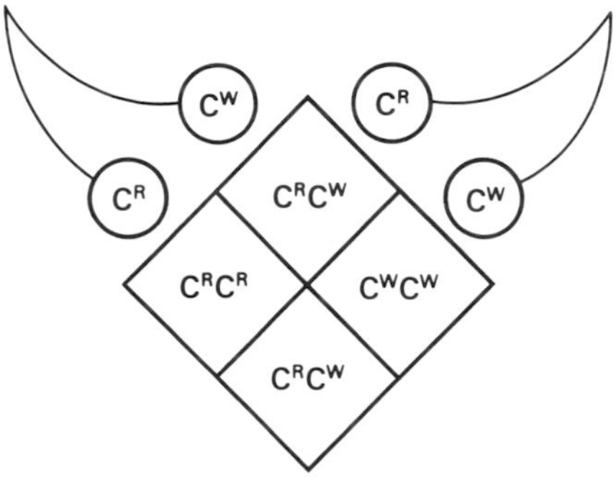
C^W
C^R
C^R
C^W
C^RC^W
C^RC^R
C^WC^W
C^RC^W

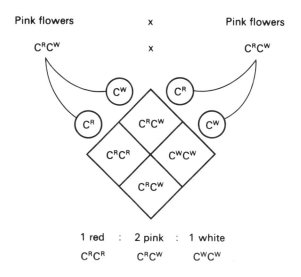

1 red : 2 pink : 1 white

C^RC^R C^RC^W C^WC^W

(b) To produce pink flowers, you must ensure that all the plants are heterozygous. This is achieved by crossing pure reds with pure whites.

Red flowers x White flowers

C^RC^R x C^WC^W

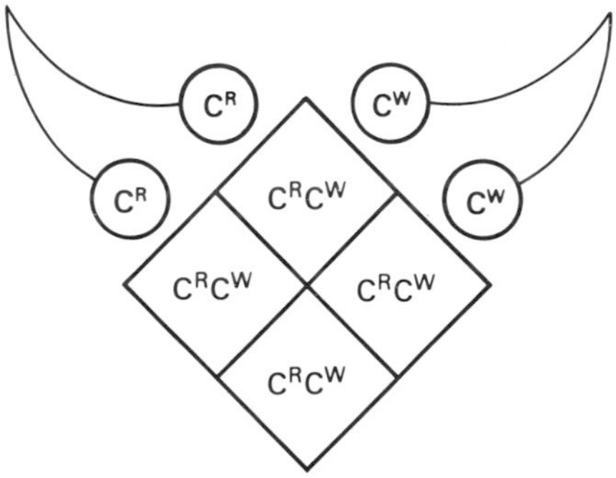
C^R
C^W
C^R
C^W
C^RC^W
C^RC^W
C^RC^W
C^RC^W

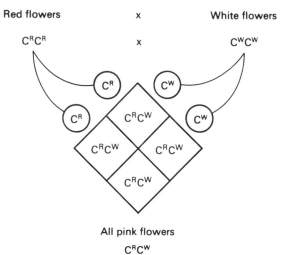

All pink flowers

C^RC^W

(c) To obtain pure reds (or pure whites) it is essential that the red (or white) plants are self-pollinated.

(i)

Red flowers x Red flowers

C^RC^R x C^RC^R

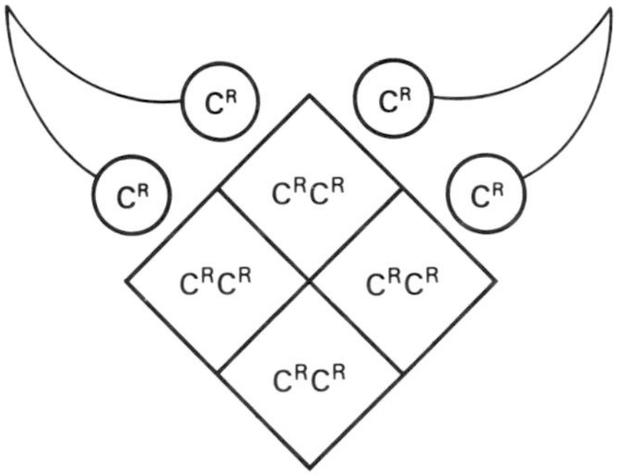
C^R
C^R
C^R
C^R
C^RC^R
C^RC^R
C^RC^R
C^RC^R

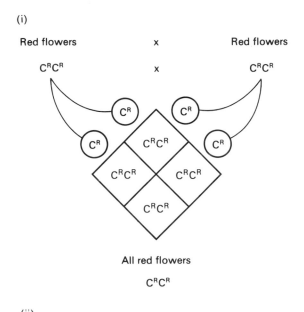

All red flowers

C^RC^R

(ii)

White flowers x White flowers

C^WC^W x C^WC^W

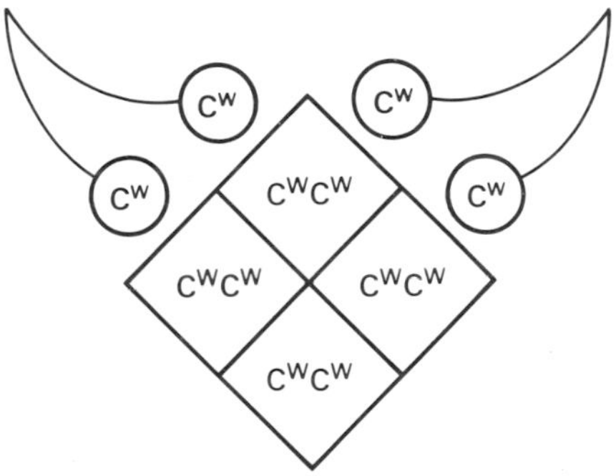
C^W
C^W
C^W
C^W
C^WC^W
C^WC^W
C^WC^W
C^WC^W

All white flowers

C^WC^W

Crossing	pink x red
Ratio	pink : red 50 : 50
Crossing	pink x white
Ratio	pink : white 50 : 50

3. *Disputed paternity*

(a) The colourblind farmer must be X^cY where X^c is the defective chromosome and I^A and I^B are codominant.
Therefore the farmers gametes are as follows:

X^cI^A, X^cI^B, YI^A, YI^B

The offspring must be as follows:

Harry XY I^OI^O
(I^OI^O is homozygous recessive.
X chromosome must be normal.)

Barry XY I^AI^O
(X chromosome must be normal.)

Carrie X^cX^c I^BI^O
(must have two defective X^c chromosomes.)

Both Barry and Carrie must carry an I^O allele which they inherited from their mother.
So the farmer could be the father of Barry and Carrie.

(b) The farmer's wife must be a carrier of colourblindness, otherwise the daughter, Carrie, would have normal vision. (The X^c chromosome from the father would be masked by a normal X chromosome.)

Farmer		Wife
(colour blind, bloodgroup AB)	x	(normal vision, bloodgroup O)
X^cY I^AI^B	x	X^cX^C I^OI^O

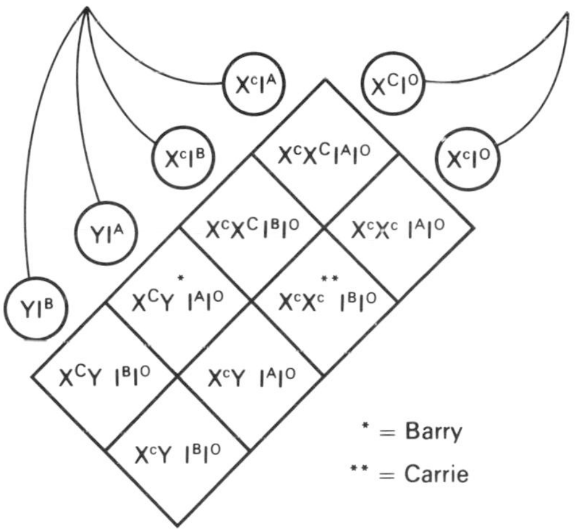

XcIA
XcIB
YIA
YIB
XCIO
XcIO
XcXCIAIO
XcXCIBIO
XcXc IAIO
XCY* IAIO
XcXc** IBIO
XCY IBIO
XcY IAIO
XcY IBIO
* = Barry
** = Carrie

50% blood group A

1 normal vision female (carrier) I^A I^O X^c X^C	1 colourblind female I^A I^O X^c X^c	1 normal vision male I^A I^O X^C Y	1 colourblind male I^A I^O X^c Y

50% blood group B

1 normal vision female (carrier) I^B I^O X^c X^C	1 colourblind female I^B I^O X^c X^c	1 normal vision male I^B I^O X^C Y	1 colourblind male I^B I^O X^c Y

4. *More about cats*

(a) Since black and ginger are codominant and lined to X chromosome:

X^G = Ginger and X^B = Black (X^GX^B = tortoiseshell)

Key Female = ♀ Male = ♂

(a)

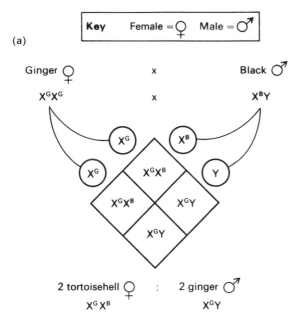

Ginger ♀ x Black ♂

X^GX^G x X^BY

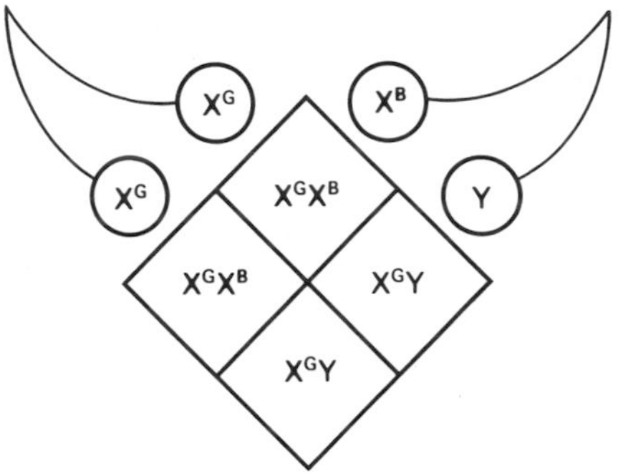

XG
XG
XB
Y
XGXB
XGXB
XGY
XGY

2 tortoisehell ♀ : 2 ginger ♂

X^GX^B X^GY

(b) (i)

Black ♀ x Ginger ♂

X^BX^B x X^GY

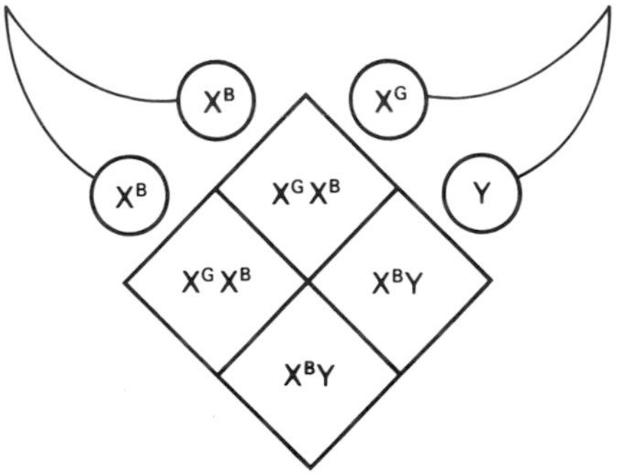

XB
XB
XG
Y
XG XB
XG XB
XBY
XBY

2 tortoisehell ♀ : 2 black ♂

X^GX^B X^BY

(b) (ii)

Tortoiseshell ♀ x Ginger ♂

X^GX^B x X^GY

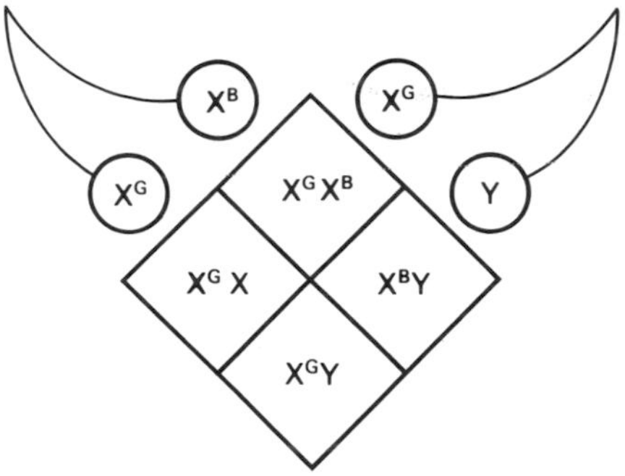

XB
XG
XG
Y
XGXB
XG X
XBY
XGY

1 ginger ♀ : 1 ginger ♂ : 1 tortoiseshell ♀ : 1 black ♂

(b) (iii)

Tortoiseshell ♀ x Black ♂

X^GX^B x X^BY

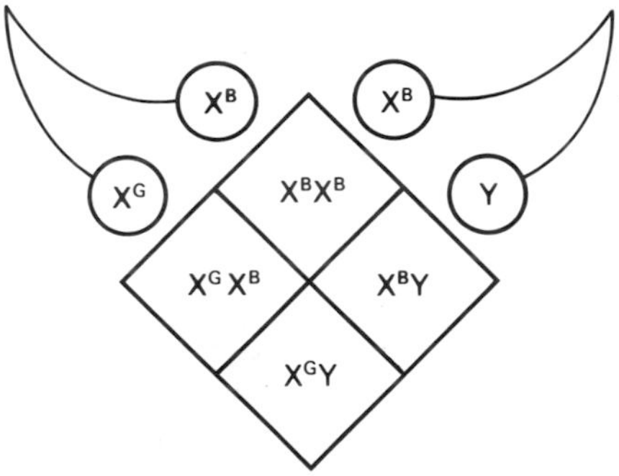

XB
XG
XB
Y
XBXB
XG XB
XBY
XGY

1 black ♀ : 1 black ♂ : 1 tortoiseshell ♀ : 1 ginger ♂

(c) The tortoiseshell male must have an X^G and an X^B plus a Y chromosome. It is an aneuploid. Aneuploids are usually sterile, i.e. the extra chromosome cannot pair in meiosis so gametogenesis (the formation of sex cells) is impaired

Chapter 6 page 63

1. (a) Grey body and normal wing.
Since all F_1 are grey-bodied and normal-winged.

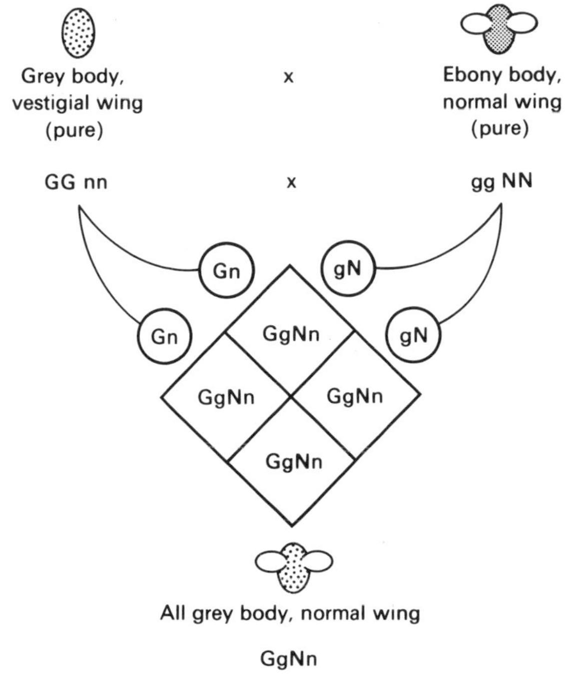
Grey body, vestigial wing (pure)
x
Ebony body, normal wing (pure)
GG nn
x
gg NN
Gn
Gn
gN
gN
GgNn
GgNn
GgNn
GgNn
All grey body, normal wing
GgNn

(b) The dominant alleles are grey body (G) and normal wing (N).

(c) Grey body and normal wing = 18
Grey body and vestigal wing = 6
Ebony body and normal wing = 6
Ebony body and vestigal wing = 2

Ratio 18 : 6 : 6 : 2
or 9 : 3 : 3 : 1

d)

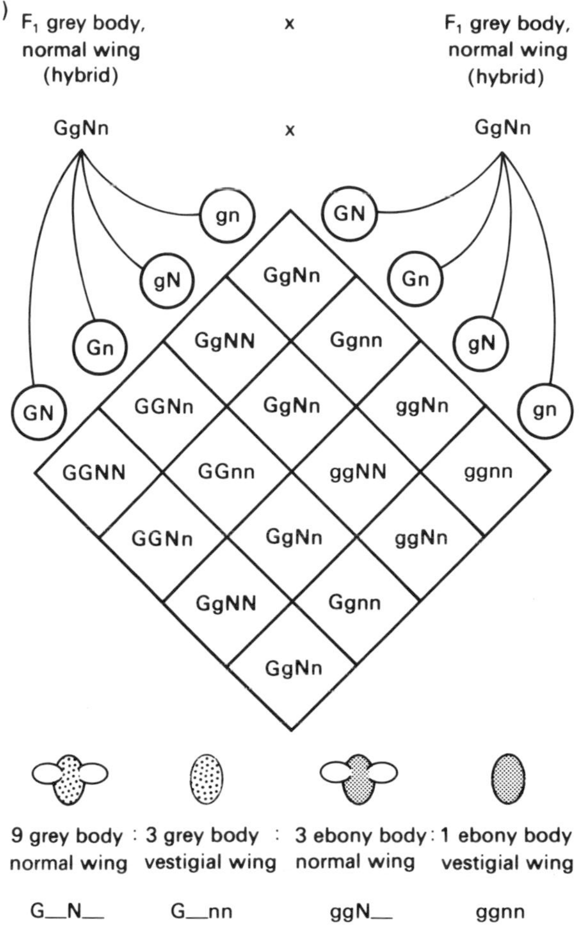
F1 grey body, normal wing (hybrid)
x
F1 grey body, normal wing (hybrid)
GgNn
x
GgNn
gn
gN
Gn
GN
GN
Gn
gN
gn
GgNn
GgNN
Ggnn
GGNn
GgNn
ggNn
GGNN
GGnn
ggNN
ggnn
GGNn
GgNn
ggNn
GgNN
Ggnn
GgNn
9 grey body normal wing
3 grey body vestigial wing
3 ebony body normal wing
1 ebony body vestigial wing
G_N_
G_nn
ggN_
ggnn

e) A ratio of 9:3:3:1 is observed in this cross. If the genes were linked, this ratio would not be observed.

2. Let S = Short fur and s = Long fur
B = Black coat and b = White coat

(a)

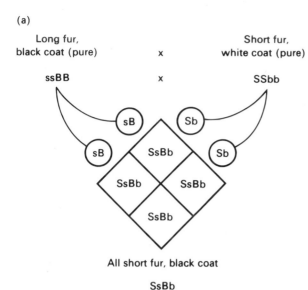

Long fur, black coat (pure)	x	Short fur, white coat (pure)
ssBB	x	SSbb

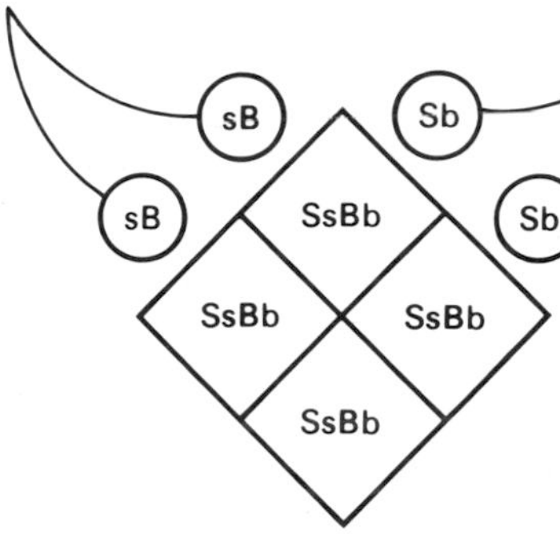
sB
sB
Sb
Sb
SsBb
SsBb
SsBb
SsBb

All short fur, black coat

SsBb

(b)

F_1 short fur, black coat (hybrid)	x	F_1 short fur, black coat (hybrid)
SsBb	x	SsBb

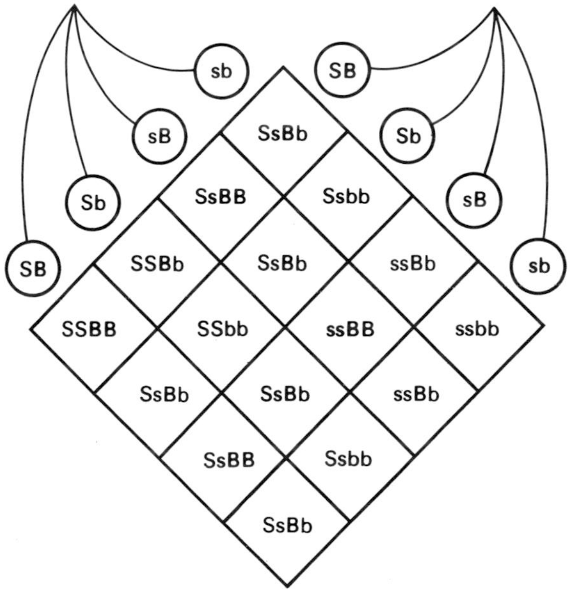
sb
sB
Sb
SB
SB
Sb
sB
sb
SsBb
SsBB
Ssbb
SSBb
SsBb
ssBb
SSBB
SSbb
ssBB
ssbb
SsBb
SsBb
ssBb
SsBB
Ssbb
SsBb

9 short fur black coat	:	3 short fur white coat	:	3 long fur black coat	:	1 long fur white coat
S__B__		S__bb		ssB__		ssbb

(c) Short fur, black coat = S–B–
When crossed with long white fur coat (i.e. ssbb) they produce all short fur.
Therefore, S– must be SS

To produce black and white coats, B– must be Bb. Therefore, the genotype of this F_2 offspring is SSBb.

TEST CROSS

F_2 short fur, black coat	x	Long fur, white coat
SSBb	x	ssbb

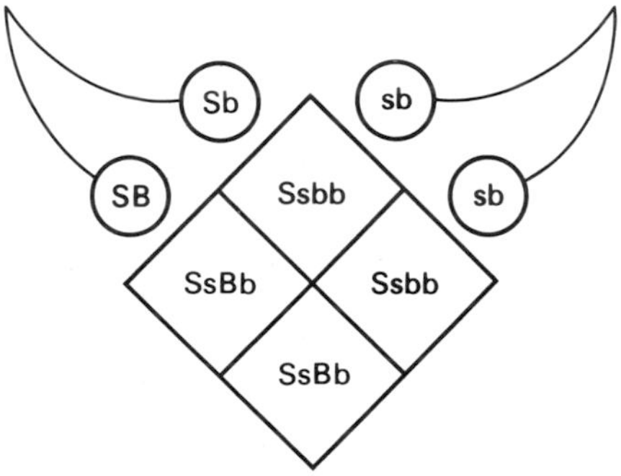
Sb
SB
sb
sb
Ssbb
SsBb
Ssbb
SsBb

50% short fur, black coat	50% short fur, white coat
SB	Sb

Chapter 6 page 63

3. (a) Mutant 2. This plant cannot make enzyme B but can make enzyme A.
(b) (i) Purple. M_1 and M_2 allow production of both red and blue pigments since both enzymes A and B can be made.

(ii) Purple x Purple

M_1m_1 M_2m_2 x M_1m_1 M_2m_2

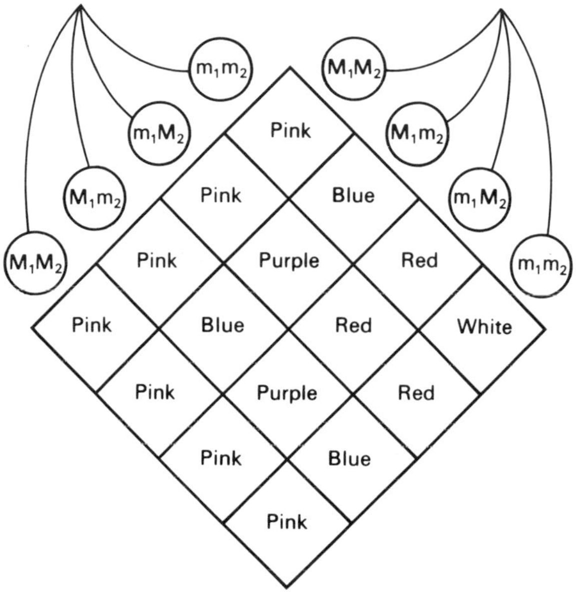

m1m2
M1M2
m1M2
M1m2
M1m2
m1M2
M1M2
m1m2
Pink
Pink
Blue
Pink
Purple
Red
Pink
Blue
Red
White
Pink
Purple
Red
Pink
Blue
Pink

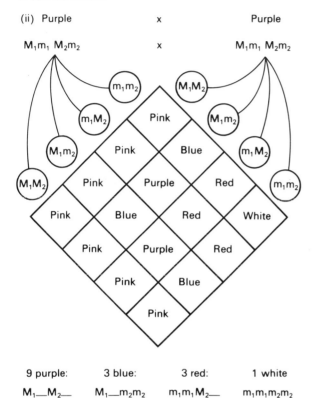

9 purple:	3 blue:	3 red:	1 white
M_1__M_2__	M_1__m_2m_2	$m_1m_1M_2$__	$m_1m_1m_2m_2$

(c) The absence of the gene leads to the absence of the enzyme so no pigment is made.

Chapter 6 page 65

1. Solution to the case of the red and white flowers

Red flower x Red flower

AaBb x AaBb

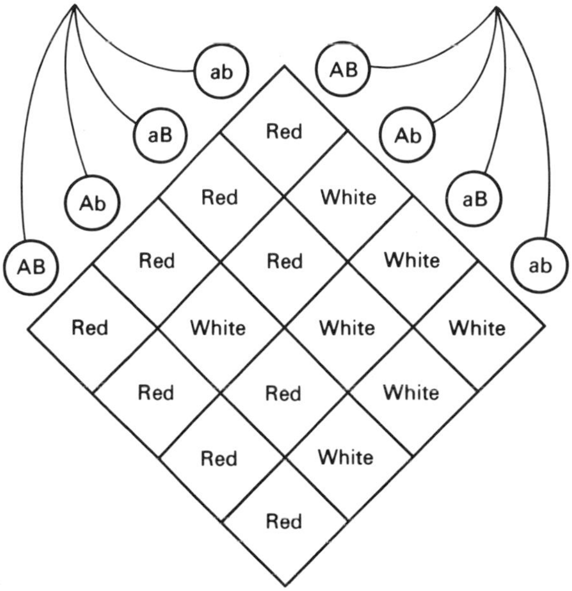

ab
AB
aB
Ab
Ab
aB
AB
ab
Red
Red
White
Red
Red
White
Red
White
White
White
Red
Red
White
Red
White
Red

Expected ratio:	9 red:	7 white
	A__B__	aa__

Chapter 7 page 77

Observed	*Expected*	*O – E*	$(O-E)^2$	$\frac{(O-E)^2}{E}$
315	312.75	2.25	5.0625	0.1619
101	104.25	-3.25	10.5625	0.1013
108	104.25	3.75	14.0625	0.1349
32	34.75	-2.75	7.5625	0.2176
556			37.25	0.6157

$$\chi^2 = \Sigma \frac{(O-E)^2}{E} = 0.6157$$

Degrees of freedom = 3   Probability lies close to 0.92, i.e. a very close fit.

Chapter 7 page 79

(a) Total population = 356 + 519 + 225 = 1100
Let M be represented by q

$$q^2 = \text{mm}$$

$$\text{Therefore } q = \sqrt{\frac{356}{1100}} = \frac{356}{1100}$$

$$= 0.569$$

Let N be represented by p

$$p^2 = \text{NN}$$

$$\text{Therefore } p = \sqrt{\frac{225}{1100}} = \frac{225}{1100}$$

$$= 0.452$$

If $p + q = 1$

and assuming equilibrium

$$p = 1 - \text{q}$$

$$= 1 - 0.569$$

$$= 0.431$$

The discrepancy indicates that it is not in equilibrium

If $q = 0.569$

and $p = 0.431$

then MN $= 2pq$

$= 2 \times 0.569 \times 0.431$

$= 0.490 = 0.539$

NN $= p^2 = 0.431 \times 0.431$

$= 0.186 = 205$

MM $= q^2 = 0.569 \times 0.569$

$= 0.324 = 356$

(b) No.

Note: where a page number for a word is shown in bold, an explanation or definition can be found in the text.

A, B, AB and O blood group 55
Acetabularia sp. 16
active site 6
adaptive radiation 93
AIDS 48
albinism **4**, 9, 31, 32
alkaptonuria 4, 5, 9
alleles **32**, 39
allelomorphism 64
allopolyploidy **11**
anaphase 21, 23-24
aneuploidy 11, 52
anticodon 7, 8
artificial selection 44
assortment, independent 77
autopolyploidy **11**
autosomal recessive allele 34
autosomes 27, 46
Avery, O.T. 13-14

balanced polymorphism 92
banded snail (*Cepaea nemoralis*) 90
benign 21
bivalents 28
blending 41
brown trout 91

callus 26
cancer 21
carriers 35, 44, 47
cat, domestic (*Felix catus*) 94
cat, wild (*Felix sylvestris*) 94
cell division 21
centromere 23, 24
Chase, Martha 14-15
Chi squared (χ^2) 74
chiasmata (with crossing over) 29
chorionic villus sampling 84
chromatids 23-24, 27
chromosomal mutations 11
chromosome map 72
chromosomes **10**, 22-24, 27
cline 93
clone 21,93
codominance 41
codon 7
colour blindness 44, 47
coupling 66
Crick, Francis 15, 17-18
cross-over value 72
crossing over 29, 68, 70
cystic fibrosis 31, 34-35

Darwin, Charles 41, 44, 89, 95, 96
Darwinism 89
density gradient centrifugation 18, **19**
deoxyribose nucleic acid, *see* DNA
diabetes 86
differentiation **25**
dihybrid inheritance 59
dihybrid ratio 63
dilution 41
diploid 1, **11**, 22
DNA (deoxyribose nucleic acid) 1, 5, 7, 15-17, 25-27, 31-32, 50, 84, 96
DNA polymorphism 83
DNA probes 36, 49, 50, 84
dominant **32**, 39
double helix 2
Down's syndrome 11, 54

emasculated 38
embryo 19, 22, 25-26
embryo testing 48-49
environmental resistance 89
enzymes **4**, 5, 81
epistasis 65
eugenics 36
euploidy 54
evolution 88

Factor VIII 48
fate maps 25
Felix catus (domestic cat) 94
Felix sylvestris (wild cat) 94
fetus 19, 79, 84
finches, Darwin's 93
fish-farming 51
Franklin, Rosalind 1-2

Galapagos Islands 89, 93
gametes 19, 27
gel electrophoresis 82
gene **10**, 26
gene mutations 11
gene probe 83
gene tracking 81, 84, 86
genetic code 7, 9
genetic counselling 45
genetic drift 94
genetic fingerprinting 36, 50, 81, 83, 96
genotype 29, **32**
gonads 27
Griffith, F. 12

haemoglobin 10, 31
haemophilia 47-48
haploid 27-28
Hardy-Weinberg equilibrium 74, 77, 78
heart disease 86
HeLa cell 21
helix, double 2
Henry fingerprinting system 81

Hershey, Alfred 14-15
heterogametic 50
heterozygote 31
heterozygous **32**, 40
HIV 48
homogametic 50
homologous 27
homologous chromosomes 29
homozygous **32**, 37
Human Genome Project 72, 86
human genome 44
Huntington's chorea 31, **34**-35
hybrid vigour 54
hybridisation 82
hydrogen bonds 2, 17
hypervariable regions (HVRs) 83

in vitro 13, 21
in vivo 21
independent assortment 29, 59, 66-67
inherited diseases 34
interphase 21
isoagglutinogen 55
isotope 18, **19**

Jacob-Monod 26
Jeffreys, Alec 81

karyotype 27
kilobase 82
Klinefelter's syndrome 53

Lamark, Jean-Baptiste 95
linkage 66, 70
Listeria monocytogenes 86
locus 47
lysis 14

malaria 31, 92
malignant 21
mapping 72
McCarty, M. 13-14
McLeod, C.M. 13-14
meiosis **27**-29, 31
melanin 4, 31-32
melanistic moths 90
Mendel, Gregor **37**, 64
Mendel's First Law 61
Mendelism 42
Meselson, M.S. 18
messenger RNA, *see* mRNA
metabolism 4
metaphase 21, 23, 24
Miescher 12
mitochondrial DNA 29
mitosis 22, 29
monohybrid inheritance 31, 34, 59
mRNA (messenger RNA) 6, 7-8, 16
mucus 34

multiple alleles 55
multiple choice questions 20, 30, 57, 73, 80, 97
muscular dystrophy 47
mutagens 11
mutants 11-12
Mutations 9, **11**

natural selection 44, 89-90
Neo-Darwinism 89
non-coding 83
non-disjunction 52
non-parental types 68
nuclear division 21
nucleotide **3**
Null hypothesis 76

ovary 27
ovum 19

^{32}P 14
pancreas 34
parental types 68
particulate theory 39, 42
PCR techniques 50
pea plant 37
peppered moth (*Biston betularia*) 11, 90
peptide bond 5, 7
phage 14
phenotype **32**
phenylketonuria **5**, 9, 34
poles 23, 24
polygenes 93
polymorphic markers 84
polyploidy 11, 54
Principle of Segregation 61
prophase 21, 23-24
protein synthesis 6
pure breeding 37
purines - adenine and guanine 2
pyrimidines - cytosine and thymine 2

rainbow trout 91
ratio 1:1 61, 64, 71
ratio 1:1:1:1 62, 64
ratio 2:1:1 42
ratio 3:1 42, 61
ratio 9:3:3:1 42, 60, 64
recessive **32**, 39
recombinant 69
recombinant types 68, 72
red-green colour blindness 47
repressor 26
reproductive potential 88
repulsion 66
restriction endonuclease 81
restriction fragment length polymorphisms (RFLPs) 83
restriction site 82
Rhesus-negative 79
ribonucleic acid, *see* RNA
ribonucleic acid polymerase 6
ribosomal RNA, *see* rRNA
ribosome 6, 8
RNA (ribonucleic acid) 6
RNA polymerase enzyme 8
root tips 24
rRNA (ribosomal RNA) 7

^{35}S 14
semi-conservative replication 17, 19
sex chromosomes 27, 46-47
sex linkage 46-47
sickle cell anaemia **10**-11, 30, 40, 45, 92
Southern blotting 82
sperm 19
spindle fibre 23
squirrel, red and grey 94
SRY (male-determining factor) 46
Stahl, F.W. 18
Streptococcus pneumonii 12
supermales 52
survival of the fittest 89

telophase 21, 23
test cross 40, 59, 61, 62, 71
testis 27
thalassaemia 45
On The Origin of Species 89
thrush's anvil 90
thyroid 5
totipotency 25
tracers 14
transcription 6
transfer RNA, *see* tRNA
transforming principle 13
translation 7
triploid 51
trisomy 54
tRNA (transfer RNA) 7, 8
tumour 21
Turner's syndrome 53
tyrosine 4
tyrosinosis 4-5, 9, 34

universal donors 56
universal recipients 56
uracil 6

Watson, James 1, 15, 17, 18
Wilkins, Maurice 1

X-ray diffraction 2
χ^2 (Chi squared) 74

zygote 19, 22